Elementary General Topology

PRENTICE-HALL MATHEMATICS SERIES

ALBERT A. BENNETT, *editor*

PRENTICE-HALL INTERNATIONAL, INC., *London*
PRENTICE-HALL OF AUSTRALIA, PTY., LTD., *Sydney*
PRENTICE-HALL OF CANADA, LTD., *Toronto*
PRENTICE-HALL OF INDIA (PRIVATE) LTD., *New Delhi*
PRENTICE-HALL OF JAPAN, INC., *Tokyo*
PRENTICE-HALL DE MEXICO, S.A., *Mexico City*

Elementary General Topology

THERAL O. MOORE

DEPARTMENT OF MATHEMATICS
UNIVERSITY OF FLORIDA

PRENTICE-HALL, INC., Englewood Cliffs, N.J.

Library of Congress Catalog Card Number: 64-23234

Printed in the United States of America

C-25690

to Nancy

Preface

The fundamentals of general topology are basic to modern analysis. Furthermore, abstract algebra and general topology are increasingly recognized as essential for the mathematics major. Some difference of opinion exists as to when topology should be introduced to the student.

After observing my undergraduate students in topology for several years, I am convinced that the fullest understanding and the greatest economy in effort result when the student follows an early course in abstract algebra by a course in topology before he studies advanced calculus or real analysis. It seems that a background in topology greatly simplifies his work in advanced calculus, while a background in the latter does not noticeably simplify his work in topology.

Topology for the undergraduate is not something for the honor student only, but benefits the general mathematics major and the mathematics education student. The idea that mathematical maturity is a prerequisite for a study of topology is widely replaced by the belief that such a study provides an excellent opportunity to attain rapid maturity.

For the reasons given above I have written this book with the undergraduate in mind. Many items (from set theory and topology) which might be difficult to the inexperienced student if introduced at the earliest logical entry place, are postponed. Often these items are very simple to the student after he is more experienced.

In Chapter 2, I begin the study of topology with the general topological space (rather than a metric space or the space of reals) for three reasons.

First, I feel that the early theorems are, in fact, easier for the undergraduate to prove for the general topological space than for the space of reals or for metric spaces. Second, there is a real economy in proving the general theorems and then applying them to the special spaces. Third, the student who has chosen mathematics as a major and who has studied abstract algebra can appreciate the abstract space from the outset and will realize the motivation soon after the general theory is applied to the special cases. Applications to the space of reals are stressed in this book.

The rigor of this text is adequate for graduate students who have not had a course in topology, and this material has been used as a text for these students as well as for undergraduates. Chapters 1 through 3, the first five sections of Chapter 4, and the first section of Chapter 5 can be covered in a one-semester undergraduate course.

Throughout this book it is emphasized that the student should give his own proofs of the exercises and many of the theorems before reading the proofs given in the text. This is an attempt to build into the book some of the features of the popular "do-it-yourself" types of courses in topology (where the class proves all the theorems). This text is intended to speed progress and to offer polished proofs with which the student may compare his own proofs. The "do-it-yourself" method may be used to cover some topics omitted from the text.

I am especially grateful to Professor W. L. Strother, who read parts of the manuscript and made valuable comments. I am also grateful to Professor R. G. Blake for many discussions concerning the manuscript.

I am grateful to many of my students who have given me great pleasure by their enthusiasm, interest, and success.

I am indebted to Professors L. M. Blumenthal, P. B. Burcham, W. R. Utz, V. W. Adkisson, and D. P. Richardson for invaluable assistance when I was a student.

THERAL O. MOORE

Gainesville, Florida

Contents

1

Elementary Set Theory

1. Sets and Subsets

A precise, sophisticated development of set theory will not be given here. Rather, we give some of the language and ideas from set theory which are essential to our present work and to abstract mathematics in general.

The word *set* will be used as an undefined term. However, we may associate with the phrase "set of things" an intuitive idea of a collection of things, and we shall use the words "set" and "collection" synonymously—though certainly without defining either! "Class" and "family" are sometimes used as synonyms for "set".

Let A denote a particular collection of objects. Each member of this collection is called an *element of A*. (Thus if A denotes the set of all books on a given shelf, the elements of A are the individual books on that shelf.) Now if x denotes a specific object, exactly one of the following statements is correct:

    (1) x is an element of A (indicated by $x \in A$),

or

    (2) x is not an element of A (written $x \notin A$).

The notation $\{a, b, g, k\}$ denotes the set consisting of the objects represented by the symbols listed and no other objects. Thus {Arkansas, Florida, Missouri} denotes the set consisting of the things which the writer represents by the symbols listed. (Naturally the writer is using the last symbols listed to represent three states in the United States.)

The notation $\{x: \ P(x)\}$, where $P(x)$ is a statement concerning x, denotes the set of all x's for which $P(x)$ is true and no other objects. This notation is read "the set of all x's such that $P(x)$". Of course a letter other than "x" may be used at times. Thus $\{y: \ y$ is a real number greater than 4} denotes the set of all real numbers greater than 4, and $\{p: \ p$ is a person now in Florida} denotes the set of all people now in Florida.

If A and B are sets, B is said to be a *subset of A* if and only if each element of B is also an element of A. We indicate that B is a subset of A by writing $B \subset A$ (read "B is contained in A"), or by writing $A \supset B$ (read "A contains B"). We formally state this definition using language to be adopted henceforth. We use "iff" as an abbreviation for "if and only if". (The reader should be sure to note that "if and only if" means more than just "if".)

Definition 1.1. Let A and B be sets. Then $B \subset A$ iff $x \in B$ implies $x \in A$.

[We shall use $A, C \subset B$ to mean $A \subset B$ and $C \subset B$; similarly, $x, y \in A$ means $x \in A$ and $y \in A$.]

Definition 1.2. Two sets A and B are said to be *equal* (written $A = B$) iff $A \subset B$ and $B \subset A$.

In view of 1.1, $\{a, d\} \subset \{a, b, d, h\}$ and $\{2, 5, 7\} \subset \{2, 5, 7\}$ even though $\{2, 5, 7\} = \{2, 5, 7\}$. In general, 1.1 gives: if A is a set, then $A \subset A$. Finally we note that

$$\{x: \ x \text{ is a positive integer less than } 2\} = \{1\}.$$

Throughout this book we shall reserve certain letters to denote specific sets as indicated:

Notation 1.3.

$R = \{x: \ x$ is a real number}, $\qquad N = \{x: \ x$ is a positive integer},

$N_k = \{x: \ x \in N$ and $x \leq k\}$, where $k \in N$,

$Q = \{x: \ x \in R$ and $0 \leq x \leq 1\}$, $\qquad I = \{x: \ x \in R$ and $0 < x < 1\}$.

In the natural course of events we frequently write $\{x: \ P(x)\}$, where it may turn out that there is no x for which $P(x)$ is true; for example, consider $\{x: \ x \in N \text{ and } x < k\}$, where k is some positive integer. If $k = 1$, it turns out that there is no x such that x is a positive integer and $x < k$. So it is convenient to introduce a set which has no elements; we call this set the *null set*, *void set*, or *empty set* and denote it by $\varnothing$.

Note that 1.1 gives: if A is a set, then $\varnothing \subset A$.

In a particular mathematical discussion there is usually a set which consists of all primary elements under consideration. For lack of a better term, we shall call this set the *underlying set* and denote it by S throughout sections 1 and 2 of this chapter. We shall be concerned with subsets of S and with collections of subsets of S.

(In a study of the system of real numbers, the underlying set S would be R, and we would have occasions to mention various subsets of R such as Q, I, or the set of all rational numbers. If one is studying Euclidean plane geometry, then S would be the set of all points in the Euclidean plane.)

Definition 1.4.   Let $A, B \subset S$. Then $\{x: \ x \in A \text{ and } x \notin B\}$ is called the *complement of B relative to A* and is denoted by $A \sim B$. The set $S \sim B$ is simply called the *complement of B*.

Exercises 1.5

1. List the eight subsets of $\{a, b, c\}$.

2. If the underlying set S is the set of all people now in the United States, what is the complement of

    (a) the set of all people now in Florida,

    (b) $\{x: \ x$ is a person now in Florida or x is a person now in Georgia$\}$?

3. Let $A = \{1, 2, 3, 4\}$, $B = \{1, 2\}$, $C = \{4, 5\}$.   What is the set

    (a) $A \sim B$,   (c) $B \sim A$,

    (b) $A \sim C$,   (d) $B \sim C$?

4. Let A be any subset of the underlying set S. What is the complement of

    (a) S,   (b) $\varnothing$,   (c) $(S \sim A)$?

Answers and proofs for many exercises in this book are given following the sets of exercises. It should be emphasized that the student should do these exercises before reading the answers in the book. Also he should receive the greatest pleasure in trying his hand at proving some of the theorems in the text before reading the proofs given. This is his most valuable mathematical experience, and soon he should be able to give his own proofs for some "very good" theorems. The following theorem gives the answer to 4(c) in 1.5.

Theorem 1.6.   If $A \subset S$, then $S \sim (S \sim A) = A$.

Proof. Suppose $p \in A$. Then

$$p \notin S \sim A, \qquad\qquad\qquad\qquad \text{(Def 1.4)}$$

and so

$$p \in S \sim (S \sim A) \qquad\qquad\qquad \text{(Def 1.4)}.$$

Therefore

(3) $$A \subset S \sim (S \sim A) \qquad\qquad\qquad \text{(Def 1.1)}.$$

Now suppose $q \in S \sim (S \sim A)$. Then $q \notin S \sim A$ and so $q \in A$. Hence

(4) $$S \sim (S \sim A) \subset A \qquad\qquad\qquad \text{(Def 1.1)}.$$

Therefore

$$S \sim (S \sim A) = A \qquad\qquad [(3), (4), (\text{Def } 1.2)].$$

Theorem 1.7.   Let $A, B \subset S$. Then $B \subset A$ iff $S \sim A \subset S \sim B$.

Proof. Suppose $B \subset A$ and $p \in S \sim A$. Then $p \notin A$ and, by 1.1, $p \notin B$ since $B \subset A$. Hence $p \in S \sim B$. Therefore $S \sim A \subset S \sim B$, and we have proved the "only if" part of our theorem (the part obtained by writing "only if" in the place of "iff"). Changing notation we have now proved that if $C \subset D$ then $S \sim D \subset S \sim C$, and we may use this result to prove the other "half" of 1.7.

To prove the "if" part of 1.7, suppose $S \sim A \subset S \sim B$. Then from the above result (taking C to be $S \sim A$ and D to be $S \sim B$) we have

$$S \sim (S \sim B) \subset S \sim (S \sim A).$$

Thus

$$B = S \sim (S \sim B) \qquad\qquad\qquad\qquad \text{(Th 1.6)}$$

$$\subset S \sim (S \sim A) \qquad\qquad\qquad \text{(above result)}$$

$$= A \qquad\qquad\qquad\qquad \text{(Th 1.6)}.$$

Therefore $B \subset A$ and 1.7 is proved.

Theorem 1.8.   Let $A, B \subset S$.   Then $A = B$ iff $S \sim A = S \sim B$.

Proof. Suppose $A = B$.   Then (by 1.2) $B \subset A$ and, by 1.7,

(5) $$S \sim A \subset S \sim B.$$

Similarly

(6) $$S \sim B \subset S \sim A \quad \text{(since } A \subset B\text{).}$$

Therefore from (5), (6) and 1.2,

$$S \sim A = S \sim B.$$

To prove the converse suppose $S \sim A = S \sim B$.   Then

$$
\begin{aligned}
A &= S \sim (S \sim A) & \text{(Th 1.6)} \\
  &= S \sim (S \sim B) & \text{(first part 1.8)} \\
  &= B & \text{(Th 1.6).}
\end{aligned}
$$

2.   Unions and Intersections

Definition 2.1.   Let $\mathcal{C}$ be a collection of subsets of the underlying set S.

(a) The set $\{x: \ x \in A \text{ for } at \ least \ one \ A \text{ in } \mathcal{C}\}$ is called the *union* of the collection $\mathcal{C}$ and is denoted by $\bigcup \mathcal{C}$.

(b) The set $\{x: \ x \in S \text{ and } x \in A \text{ for } each \ A \text{ in } \mathcal{C}\}$ is called the *intersection* of the collection $\mathcal{C}$ and is denoted by $\bigcap \mathcal{C}$.

Notice that an element of S, say p, belongs to $\bigcup \mathcal{C}$ iff *there exists at least one A in $\mathcal{C}$ such that $p \in A$*, while $p \in \bigcap \mathcal{C}$ iff $A \in \mathcal{C}$ implies $p \in A$.

Since "$\{A: \ A \in \mathcal{C}\}$" is just another symbol for the collection $\mathcal{C}$, we may write "$\bigcup \{A: \ A \in \mathcal{C}\}$" to denote $\bigcup \mathcal{C}$.   Indeed, any symbol which denotes a collection of sets may be written after "$\bigcup$" to denote the union of the collection; similarly for intersections.

Exercises 2.2

1.   Let $S = R$, $A = \{x: \ x \in S \text{ and } 0 < x < 4\}$, $B = \{x: \ x \in S \text{ and } 1 < x \leq 3\}$ and $C = \{x: \ x \in S \text{ and } 2 < x \leq 5\}$.   Specify

(a) $\bigcup \{A, B, C\}$,

(b) $\bigcap \{A, B, C\}$.

Usually we shall use the notation $A \cup B \cup C$ for the set in (a), $A \cap B \cap C$ for the set in (b) and similar (self-explaining) notations for unions and intersections.

2. Let $A = \{-2, 0, 3, 4, 5\}$, $B = \{0, 1, 2, 3, 5\}$, $C = \{0, 6, 7\}$ and $D = \{8, 9\}$. List the elements (if there are any) of

(a) $A \cap B$,   (c) $A \cap C$,

(b) $A \cup B \cup C$,   (d) $A \cap D$.

3. Before reading 2.3, consider 2.1 and decide what $\bigcup \mathcal{C}$ is when $\mathcal{C}$ is the null collection of subsets of S. What is $\bigcap \mathcal{C}$ in case $\mathcal{C}$ is null? (See the first paragraph after 2.1.)

4. $S \sim \bigcup \mathcal{C}$ is equal to which of the sets: $\bigcup \{S \sim A: \ A \in \mathcal{C}\}$ or $\bigcap \{S \sim A: \ A \in \mathcal{C}\}$, where $\{S \sim A: \ A \in \mathcal{C}\}$ denotes $\{B: \ B = S \sim A$ for some A in $\mathcal{C}\}$. The notation introduced here will be used freely in the future.

5. What can you say about $S \sim \bigcap \mathcal{C}$?

Remark 2.3.   If $\mathcal{C}$ is the null collection of subsets of S, then

$$\text{(a)} \quad \bigcup \mathcal{C} = \varnothing \quad \text{and} \quad \text{(b)} \quad \bigcap \mathcal{C} = S.$$

Proof. (a) Suppose $p \in S$. Now in order that $p \in \bigcup \mathcal{C}$, p would have to belong to *at least one* A in $\mathcal{C}$; but this is impossible since there is no A in $\mathcal{C}$. Hence $p \notin \bigcup \mathcal{C}$. Since p was an arbitrary element of S, it follows that $\bigcup \mathcal{C} = \varnothing$.

(b) Suppose $p \in S$. Then since $\mathcal{C}$ is null, it is correct that p belongs to each member of $\mathcal{C}$. Hence, by 2.1(b), $p \in \bigcap \mathcal{C}$ and so $S \subset \bigcap \mathcal{C}$. But by 2.1(b), $\bigcap \mathcal{C} \subset S$; and therefore $\bigcap \mathcal{C} = S$.

(To convince the skeptical reader of (b), we might say that in view of 2.1(b) the only way an element p of S can fail to belong to $\bigcap \mathcal{C}$ is that there be an A in $\mathcal{C}$ such that $p \notin A$; but this cannot happen since there is no A in $\mathcal{C}$.) (Or we may say to the reader experienced in formal logic that the second sentence in the proof of (b) can be written as: "Then since $\mathcal{C}$ is null, the following proposition is true—since the hypothesis in this proposition is false: If $A \in \mathcal{C}$, then $p \in A$.")

Theorem 2.4 (DeMorgan).   If $\mathcal{C}$ is a collection of subsets of the underlying set S, then

(a) $$S \sim \bigcup \mathcal{C} = \bigcap \{S \sim A: \ A \in \mathcal{C}\}$$

and

(b) $$S \sim \bigcap \mathcal{C} = \bigcup \{S \sim A: \ A \in \mathcal{C}\}.$$

Proof. (a) Suppose $p \in S \sim \bigcup \mathcal{C}$. Then $p \notin \bigcup \mathcal{C}$, and so

$$\text{for each } A \text{ in } \mathcal{C}, \quad p \notin A \qquad\qquad \text{(Def 2.1(a)).}$$

Hence

$$\text{for each } A \text{ in } \mathcal{C}, \quad p \in S \sim A \qquad\qquad \text{(Def 1.4).}$$

Therefore

$$p \in \bigcap \{S \sim A: \quad A \in \mathcal{C}\} \qquad\qquad \text{(Def 2.1(b)),}$$

and

$$(1) \qquad\qquad S \sim \bigcup \mathcal{C} \subset \bigcap \{S \sim A: \quad A \in \mathcal{C}\} \qquad\qquad \text{(Def 1.1).}$$

Now suppose $q \in \bigcap \{S \sim A: \quad A \in \mathcal{C}\}$. Then $q \in S \sim A$ for each A in $\mathcal{C}$; so for each A in $\mathcal{C}$, $q \notin A$. Therefore $q \notin \bigcup \mathcal{C}$ so that $q \in S \sim \bigcup \mathcal{C}$. Thus

$$(2) \qquad\qquad \bigcap \{S \sim A: \quad A \in \mathcal{C}\} \subset S \sim \bigcup \mathcal{C}.$$

Consequently

$$S \sim \bigcup \mathcal{C} = \bigcap \{S \sim A: \quad A \in \mathcal{C}\} \qquad\qquad [(1), (2), 1.2].$$

(b) To prove (b) we first apply result (a) to the collection $\{S \sim A: \quad A \in \mathcal{C}\}$. We have

$$S \sim \bigcup \{S \sim A: \quad A \in \mathcal{C}\} = \bigcap \{S \sim (S \sim A): \quad A \in \mathcal{C}\} \quad \text{[Part (a)]}$$
$$= \bigcap \{A: \quad A \in \mathcal{C}\} \qquad\qquad \text{(Th 1.6)}$$
$$= \bigcap \mathcal{C}.$$

Taking complements of the first and last members of this equality, we have

$$\bigcup \{S \sim A: \quad A \in \mathcal{C}\} = S \sim \bigcap \mathcal{C}$$

and (b) is proved.

(The reader should note that each sentence in the proof of 2.4 is valid even when $\mathcal{C}$ is null.)

Exercises 2.5

Let B, C and D be subsets of the underlying set S and let $\mathcal{C}$ be a collection of subsets of S. Prove each of the following.

1. If $H \in \mathcal{C}$, then $H \subset \bigcup \mathcal{C}$. (Note the corollary: $B \subset C \cup B$.)

2. $\bigcap \mathcal{C} \subset H$ for each H in $\mathcal{C}$.

3. $B \cup C = B$ iff $C \subset B$.

4. $B \cap C = B$ iff $B \subset C$.

5. If $B \cup C = B$ and $B \cap C = B$, then $B = C$. (Use half of 3 and half of 4.)

6. The distributive property of $\cap$ over $\bigcup$:

$$B \cap (\bigcup \mathcal{C}) = \bigcup \{B \cap A: \quad A \in \mathcal{C}\}$$

where $\{B \cap A: \quad A \in \mathcal{C}\}$ denotes

$$\{X: \quad X = B \cap A \text{ for some } A \text{ in } \mathcal{C}\}.$$

(We shall use similar obvious notations in the future without explanation.)   Note the corollary:

$$B \cap (C \cup D) = (B \cap C) \cup (B \cap D).$$

7. Distributive property of $\cup$ over $\cap$:

$$B \cup (\bigcap \mathcal{C}) = \bigcap \{B \cup A: \quad A \in \mathcal{C}\}.$$

8. $B \cup (\bigcup \mathcal{C}) = \bigcup \{B \cup A: \quad A \in \mathcal{C}\}$ if $\mathcal{C}$ *is not null.*   Show that the condition that $\mathcal{C}$ be non-null is needed here but was not needed in 1, 2, 6 and 7.

9. $B \cap (\bigcap \mathcal{C}) = \bigcap \{B \cap A: \quad A \in \mathcal{C}\}$ *if* $\mathcal{C}$ *is not null.*   Is the hypothesis that $\mathcal{C}$ be non-void needed here?

3. Binary Relations: Cartesian Products and Mappings

If $x \in X$ and $y \in Y$ where X and Y are sets, we shall use (x, y) to denote the "ordered pair" whose "first member" is x and whose "second member" is y.   We say $(x, y) = (u, v)$ iff $x = u$ and $y = v$.   Thus $(x, y) \neq (y, x)$ unless $x = y$.   Hence (x, y) is not the same thing as $\{x, y\}$, for always $\{x, y\} = \{y, x\}$.

We use $\{(x, y): \quad x \in X, y \in Y\}$ to denote

$$\{w: \quad w = (x, y) \text{ for some } x \text{ in } X \text{ and some } y \text{ in } Y\},$$

i.e., the set of all ordered pairs (x, y) for x in X and y in Y.

Definition 3.1.   Let X and Y be sets.   The set

$$\{(x, y): \quad x \in X, y \in Y\}$$

is called the *Cartesian product of X and Y* and is denoted by $X \times Y$.

Of course X and Y may be the same set in many examples.   For instance, from one point of view, the set of all points in the Euclidean plane is precisely $R \times R$, where (see 1.3) R is the set of all real numbers.

Definition 3.2.   Let X and Y be sets.   Any subset E of $X \times Y$ is called a *binary relation from X to Y.*   We call E a *binary relation on X* iff $Y = X$.

Suppose $E \subset X \times Y$. We write xEy iff $(x, y) \in E$, and in this case we say that x is E-related to y or that y is an E-relative of x.

Examples 3.3.   (a) Let X be the set of all male students in a given university at a given time. Let E be the binary relation on X (i.e., $E \subset X \times X$) defined as follows: for $x, y \in X$,

$$(x, y) \in E \text{ iff } x \text{ is a brother of } y.$$

(Here we do not call a man his own brother.)

(b) Let X be the set of all men in the U.S. and Y the set of all women in the U.S. at a given time.   Let $E \subset X \times Y$ be defined so that

$$xEy \text{ iff } x \text{ is the husband of } y \text{ at the given time.}$$

(c) Let X be the set of all straight lines in the Euclidean plane, and let $E \subset X \times X$ be defined so that

$$xEy \text{ iff } x \text{ is parallel to } y.$$

Here we do not call a line parallel to itself.

(d) Let X be the same as in (c), and define E so that for $x, y \in X$,

$$(x, y) \in E \text{ iff } x \text{ is perpendicular to } y.$$

(e) Let X be a non-empty set and let c be some particular element in X. Define a binary relation E on X so that for x, y in X,

$$xEy \text{ iff } x = c \text{ or } y = c.$$

Let $E \subset X \times Y$.   The set $\{x: (x, y) \in E \text{ for some } y \text{ in } Y\}$ is called the *domain of E*.   (Clearly the domain of E is a subset of X.)   For each subset A of X, we use $E[A]$ to denote

$$\{y: (x, y) \in E \text{ for some } x \text{ in } A\}.$$

(If no element of A is in the domain of E, then $E[A]$ turns out to be the null set.)   The set $E[X]$ is called the *range of E*.

Since $X \times Y \subset X \times Y$, it follows from 3.2 that the Cartesian product $X \times Y$ is a special binary relation.   Another important type of binary relation is a mapping or function.   We usually use small letters to denote functions.

Definition 3.4.   Let X and Y be sets.   A subset f of $X \times Y$ is called a *mapping of X into Y* (or a *function on X to Y*) iff for each x in X there is exactly one y in Y such that $(x, y) \in f$.   We often denote this mapping by $f: X \longrightarrow Y$.

Thus:

Remark 3.5.   A binary relation f from X to Y is a mapping of X into Y iff

(a) $x \in X$ implies there is a y in Y such that $(x, y) \in f$,

and

(b) $(x, y) \in f$ and $(x, z) \in f$ implies $y = z$.

If we say "f associates the element y with x" iff $(x, y) \in f$, we see that a mapping f of X into Y associates with each element in X exactly one element in Y. We call y the *image of x (under f)* iff $(x, y) \in f$. For each x in X we denote the image of x under f by $f(x)$. Since the mapping f is a binary relation, the terminology and notation given in the first paragraph following 3.3 are applicable to f. If $A \subset X$, then $f[A]$ (as given in that paragraph) may be written in our special notation for functions as

$$\{y: \quad y = f(x) \text{ for some } x \text{ in } A\} \quad \text{or as} \quad \{f(x): \quad x \in A\}$$

and is called the *image of A (under f)*. Part (a) of 3.5 tells us that the domain of f is the whole set X (if f is a mapping of X into Y). Of course the range of f, i.e., $f[X]$ (which is a subset of Y) may not be equal to Y. (See 3.6(b).) If $B \subset Y$, then $\{x: \quad f(x) \in B\}$ is called the *inverse image of B (under f)* and is denoted by $f^{-1}[B]$.

A familiar example of a mapping of the set R of all real numbers into R is determined by the following criterion: For each x in R, $f(x)$ is $3x^2$. Here the mapping f is the set

$$\{(x, y): \quad x \in R \quad \text{and} \quad y = 3x^2\}.$$

Some writers call this set the "graph" of the mapping, but we call this set the mapping itself (Def 3.4). Those writers may have defined a mapping of X into Y as a "correspondence" or "rule" which associates with each element x in X a unique element $f(x)$ in Y. We do not prefer to define a mapping as a "rule" or as a "correspondence" since these terms have not been precisely defined in a mathematical sense. The reader might find himself hard pressed to give a good definition of "correspondence" if asked to do so. Ultimately he might use the idea of a subset of a Cartesian product.

Apart from aesthetic reasons, we have adopted Definition 3.4 so as to define a mapping in terms of our original undefined concept "set" (a mapping of X into Y being a certain kind of set contained in $X \times Y$). We know that in a formal mathematical system something must remain undefined. However, we like to use as few undefined terms as possible.

Although we have defined the notion of a mapping of X into Y as a certain type of subset of $X \times Y$, we usually indicate a specific example of a mapping by giving the criterion which determines for each x in X the image $f(x)$ in Y which is paired with x.

Definition 3.6.   Let f be a mapping of X into Y.

(a) f is said to be a *one-to-one* mapping (of X into Y) iff $x, z \in X$ and $x \neq z$ implies $f(x) \neq f(z)$.

(b) f is said to be a mapping of X *onto* Y iff $f[X] = Y$.

Notice that a mapping of X into Y may be one-to-one without being onto Y.   Of course it may be onto Y without being one-to-one.

Examples 3.7.   (a) Let f be the mapping of R into R defined as follows: For each x in R, $f(x) = x^3$.   This mapping is one-to-one since $a, b \in R$ and $a \neq b$ implies $a^3 \neq b^3$.   It is onto R since for each y in R there is some x in R such that $x^3 = y$.

(b) Let X be the set of all complex numbers and let $f: X \longrightarrow X$ be defined so that for each x in X, $f(x) = x^3$.   This mapping is onto X but not one-to-one (since there are three distinct elements in X each of which maps into 1 under f; they are the three cube roots of 1).

(c) Let $f: N \longrightarrow N$ be defined as follows (where N is as given in 1.3): For each x in N, let $f(x) = 2x$.   This mapping is one-to-one but not onto N since there is no x in N such that $f(x) = 5$.

Suppose f is a one-to-one mapping of X into Y.   In this case we see that for each y in $f[X]$, there is exactly one x in X such that $f(x) = y$.   Thus if we associate with each y in $f[X]$ the unique x in X such that $f(x) = y$, we determine a one-to-one mapping of $f[X]$ onto X.   This mapping is called the inverse mapping of f.

Definition 3.8.   Let $f: X \longrightarrow Y$ be a one-to-one function on X to Y. The function which associates with each y in $f[X]$ the unique x in X such that $f(x) = y$ is called the *inverse mapping* (or *inverse function*) of f and is denoted by f^{-1} or sometimes by $f^{-1}: f[X] \longrightarrow X$.

Let the reader determine the inverse mapping of the function given in 3.7(a).
We give one further definition in this section, which is of general interest.

Definition 3.9.   Let X be a set.   A subset E of $X \times X$ (i.e., a binary relation on X) is called an *equivalence relation on X* iff E is

(a) reflexive on X [for each x in X, $(x, x) \in E$],

(b) symmetric [$(x, y) \in E$ implies $(y, x) \in E$], and

(c) transitive [$(x, y) \in E$ and $(y, z) \in E$ implies $(x, z) \in E$].

Let X be the set of all integers ($X = \{0, \pm1, \pm2, \pm3, \ldots\}$), and let E be the subset of $X \times X$ defined as follows: The ordered pair (x, y) belongs to E iff there is some k in X such that $x - y = 5k$.   The reader may verify that E is an equivalence relation on X.   Also, if X is any set, then $X \times X$ is an equivalence relation on X.

Exercises 3.10

In 1–5 let X and Y be sets and let f be a mapping of X into Y.   Let $\mathcal{C}$ be a collection of subsets of X and let $\mathcal{F}$ be a family (i.e., collection) of subsets of Y.

1.   Prove:

(a) $f[\bigcup \mathcal{C}] = \bigcup \{f[A]:\ A \in \mathcal{C}\}$,

(b) $f[\bigcap \mathcal{C}] \subset \bigcap \{f[A]:\ A \in \mathcal{C}\}$.

(Note the corollary $f[B \cap C] \subset f[B] \cap f[C]$ and indicate an example in which $f[B \cap C] \neq f[B] \cap f[C]$.)

(c) $f[\bigcap \mathcal{C}] = \bigcap \{f[A]:\ A \in \mathcal{C}\}$ if f is one-to-one.

2.   Prove:

(a) $f^{-1}[\bigcup \mathcal{F}] = \bigcup \{f^{-1}[A]:\ A \in \mathcal{F}\}$ and

(b) $f^{-1}[\bigcap \mathcal{F}] = \bigcap \{f^{-1}[A]:\ A \in \mathcal{F}\}$.

3.   Let $B \subset Y$.   Prove $f[f^{-1}[B]] = B \cap f[X]$.

4.   Let $A \subset X$.   Prove $A \subset f^{-1}[f[A]]$, and give an example to show that equality need not hold.

5.   Prove $f^{-1}[f[A]] = A$ for each $A \subset X$ iff f is one-to-one.

6.   Let $X = \{a, b\}$ and $Y = \{a, c, d\}$.   List the six elements of $X \times Y$.

7.   When making examples of binary relations to satisfy specified conditions, one may make perfectly "artificial" relations just to fit his needs (as in 3.3(e)) rather than look for "natural" relations such as

"is less than", "is a brother of", "is parallel to", etc. Give an example of a binary relation on a set X which is

(a) reflexive on X and symmetric but not transitive,

(b) reflexive on X and transitive but not symmetric,

(c) symmetric and transitive but not reflexive on X.

(*Caution:* If a binary relation E is to be transitive, xEy and yEz must imply xEz even when $x = z$. In 3.9(c) nothing is said about x, y and z being distinct.)

8. (a) Show that the relations in 3.3(c) and (d) are not transitive.

(b) Under what circumstance is the relation in 3.3(a) transitive?

(c) When is the relation in 3.3(e) transitive?

9. (a) Show that the relation in 3.3(a) is transitive iff there is no pair of brothers in the given university (i.e., E is null).

(b) Show that the relation in 3.3(e) is transitive iff $X = \{c\}$ (i.e., X consists of the single element c).

10. Let E be a symmetric, transitive binary relation on a set X. Prove that E is reflexive on X if for each x in X there is some y in X such that xEy. (This makes it clear as to the type of example one must seek for 7(c). Do 7(c) before reading the next exercise.)

11. (We give here an answer to 7(c). In view of 10, we must make sure there is at least one element which has no relative at all. We "build" an "artificial" example just to fit our purpose.) Let X be a non-void set and let b be some particular element of X. Let E be the binary relation on X defined as follows: for $x, y \in X$, xEy iff $x \neq b$ and $y \neq b$. Show that E is symmetric and transitive but not reflexive on X.

4. Infinite Sets

Definition 4.1.   A set X is said to be *finite* iff it is null or there is a mapping of N_k onto X for some k in N. (See 1.3 for the meaning of N and N_k.) X is said to be *infinite* iff it is not finite.

Definition 4.2.   A set X is said to be *countable* iff it is null or there is a mapping of N onto X. A set is said to be *uncountable* iff it is not countable.

Before stating our next theorem, we comment on the system of logic which we use. Let P and W denote propositions and let P' and W' denote the negations of P and W respectively. Then each of the following statements is a proposition:

(1)   If P, then W.

(2) P implies W.

(3)   If W', then P'.

(4) W' implies P'.

Statements (1) and (2) are just two ways of saying the same thing; (3) and (4) are two ways of saying the same thing. In our work we shall consider (1) and (3) to be logically equivalent. Statement (3) is called the *contrapositive* of (1).

Theorem 4.3.   Let A and B be sets with $A \subset B$.

(a) If B is finite, then A is finite.

(b) If A is infinite, then B is infinite.

Proof. (a) In case A is void, then A is finite by 4.1. So suppose A is not null, and suppose B is finite. Then B is not null, and so there is a mapping f of N_k onto B for some k in N. Let p be some particular element in A, and define a mapping g of N_k into A as follows. For each n in N_k,

$$g(n) = \begin{cases} f(n) & \text{if } f(n) \in A \\ p & \text{if } f(n) \notin A. \end{cases}$$

Clearly g is a mapping of N_k onto A (since f is onto B) and (a) is proved.

(b) The proposition in (b) is simply the contrapositive of the one in (a) since "A is infinite" is the negation of "A is finite" and similarly for B.

Let the reader prove the following theorem.

Theorem 4.4.   Let A and B be sets with $A \subset B$.

(a) If B is countable, then A is countable.

(b) If A is uncountable, then B is uncountable.

Remark 4.5.   The set N is countable.

Proof. The "identity mapping" f of N into N defined by $f(x) = x$ for each x in N is clearly a mapping of N onto N. Hence N is countable by 4.2.

Corollary 4.6.   Each subset of N is countable.

Theorem 4.7.   Let f be a mapping of a set A onto a set B.

(a) If A is finite, then B is finite.

(b) If A is countable, then B is countable.

Proof. (a) If $B \neq \varnothing$ and A is finite, then there is a mapping g of N_k onto A for some k in N.   For each x in N_k define

$$h(x) = f(g(x)).$$

Thus we have a mapping h of N_k *onto* B.   (The reader should verify that h is onto B.)   Hence B is finite.

(b) The proof of (b) is similar to that of (a).

The mapping h used in the above proof is called the composition mapping of g and f.   Since composition mappings are used frequently, we give the following definition.

Definition 4.8.   If $g\colon\; X \longrightarrow Y$ and $f\colon\; Y \longrightarrow Z$ are mappings, then the mapping $h\colon\; X \longrightarrow Z$ defined by

$$h(x) = f(g(x)) \quad \text{for each} \quad x \text{ in } X$$

is called the *composition mapping of g and f* (or *g followed by f*) and is denoted by $f \circ g$.

Exercises 4.9

1.   Prove that each finite set is countable.

2.   Let f be a one-to-one mapping of a set A into a set B.   Prove: If A is infinite, then B is infinite.

3.   Let f be a one-to-one mapping of a set A into a set B.   Prove: If B is countable, then A is countable.

Preparatory for the next theorem we observe that a real number may or may not have two different decimal representations (by our usual method of representing numbers in decimal form).   For instance $7.320000\ldots$ and $7.31999\ldots$ represent the same number, while $4.963333\ldots$ is the only decimal representation (in the usual form) for the number which it does represent.   The important observation for us is that if a number has two different decimal representations, then one of these representations repeats

0's from some place onward and the other repeats 9's from some place onward.

Theorem 4.10.   The set R of all real numbers is uncountable.

Proof.   Let f be *any* mapping of N into R.   (We shall show that $f[N] \neq R$, i.e., f is not onto R; and since f is an *arbitrary* mapping of N into R, it will follow that there is *no* mapping of N onto R and that R is uncountable.) Let each element in R have a definite decimal representation.   Let r be the real number whose representation is $3.d_1 d_2 d_3 \ldots d_n \ldots$, where for each n in N, $d_n = 4$ if the nth decimal place in our representation of the number $f(n)$ is 7 and $d_n = 7$ otherwise.   Thus, for each n in N, the number r differs from $f(n)$ in the nth decimal place.   But r has only one decimal representation since the given one has no 9's and no 0's.   Therefore, for each n in N, $f(n) \neq r$, so that $r \notin f[N]$.   Hence f is not onto R, and R is uncountable.

Theorem 4.11.   The set $N \times N$ is countable.

Proof.   Let $A = \{x: \ x = 2^n 3^m \text{ for } n, m \in N\}$.   Then $A \subset N$, and so A is countable by 4.6.   We now define a mapping f of A into $N \times N$.   If $x \in A$, then there is exactly one pair n, m in N such that $x = 2^n 3^m$.   For each x in A we define $f(x)$ to be that pair (n, m) in $N \times N$ such that $x = 2^n 3^m$. The mapping thus defined is clearly a mapping of the countable set A *onto* $N \times N$.   Therefore $N \times N$ is countable by 4.7(b).

Theorem 4.12.   The union of a countable collection of countable sets is countable.

Proof.   Let C be a countable collection of sets each of which is countable. If $\bigcup C = \varnothing$, then this union is countable by Def 4.2.   Suppose then that $\bigcup C \neq \varnothing$, and let $\mathcal{B}$ denote the collection of all non-void members of C.

Since $\mathcal{B} \subset C$, $\mathcal{B}$ is countable; and (since $\mathcal{B}$ is non-null) there is a mapping, say f, of N *onto* $\mathcal{B}$.   So

$$\mathcal{B} = \{f(1), f(2), \ldots, f(n), \ldots\} = \{A_1, A_2, \ldots, A_n, \ldots\}$$

if we denote the set $f(n)$ by A_n for each n in N.   For each n in N, A_n is a non-empty countable set.   Thus, for each n in N, there is a mapping, say g_n, of N *onto* A_n.   If we denote the image of m under g_n by a_{nm}, then

$$A_1 = \{a_{11}, a_{12}, a_{13}, \ldots, a_{1m}, \ldots\}$$
$$A_2 = \{a_{21}, a_{22}, a_{23}, \ldots, a_{2m}, \ldots\}$$
$$\ldots$$
$$A_n = \{a_{n1}, a_{n2}, a_{n3}, \ldots, a_{nm}, \ldots\}$$
$$\ldots\ldots$$

We now define a mapping h of $N \times N$ into $\bigcup \mathcal{B}$. For each (n, m) in $N \times N$, let $h((n, m))$ be a_{nm} (which is an element of A_n).

The reader should verify that h is onto $\bigcup \mathcal{B}$. Now since $N \times N$ is countable, it follows from 4.7(b) that $\bigcup \mathcal{B}$ is countable. Finally, since $\bigcup \mathcal{C} = \bigcup \mathcal{B}$, we have $\bigcup \mathcal{C}$ is countable.

Exercises 4.13

1. Prove the set of all positive rational numbers is countable.

2. Prove the set of all rational numbers is countable.

3. A circle in the Euclidean plane is said to have a *rational center* iff both coordinates of its center are rational numbers. Prove that the set of all circles in the Euclidean plane with rational radii and rational centers is countable.

5. Set Theory and the Foundations of Mathematics

In the preceding sections we have tried to give the bare essentials from set theory necessary for the very beginning of a sane study of topology. We have tried to do so with a minimum of motivating commentary, which would tend to clutter up our presentation and obscure our main precise ideas—thus distracting from the clarity and beauty of these concepts and the theory as a whole.

Now that the student is thoroughly familiar with the concepts presented, we feel he may enjoy, and benefit from, a discussion of some factors which motivated us in our choice of topics and particular definitions. A glance at the definition of a topology (Ch 2, 1.1) as a certain kind of collection of sets makes it clear as to why some knowledge of set theory is a must for a study of topology. But what is more profound, set theory is basic for the whole of modern mathematics.

Set theory and logic constitute the foundations of mathematics. The development of set theory was initiated by the research of George Cantor around 1870, and Cantor is generally regarded as the founder of set theory. A most remarkable claim for set theory is that all present-day mathematics can be derived from the concept of a set.

We know that in a formal mathematical system (i.e., an axiomatic system) one begins with some undefined (or primitive) terms and some axioms concerning these primitive terms and then proceeds by laying down definitions and using logic to derive conclusions from the axioms. The remarkable claim of the last paragraph is that the collection of primitive terms for all mathematics of today may be reduced to the primitive terms in set theory (and it has been claimed that the primitive terms in set theory may be reduced to a single term).

Let us indicate briefly how one particular part of mathematics may be built upon the concept of set as a foundation. The Euclidean plane E_2 may be considered as the Cartesian product $R \times R$ together with a certain distance function on $E_2 \times E_2$ which assigns to each element (p, q) in $E_2 \times E_2$ a non-negative real number called the distance from p to q. We see then that this approach to the Euclidean plane involves real numbers, Cartesian products and a function (or mapping). Even our brief treatment of set theory has indicated that Cartesian products and mappings are just certain kinds of sets. So if the system of real numbers can be built in such a way that it rests upon the set concept, then the Euclidean plane can be made to rest upon this concept. Indeed the system of real numbers can be so developed, and this development is itself considered a part of set theory. Such development here would too long delay our study of topology.

Of course for a program which makes all mathematics rest on the concept of set, set theory itself must be developed on an axiomatic basis. By "a precise, sophisticated development" in our opening sentence of this chapter we mean an axiomatic development. (Such development is not given here.)

We hope that by now the student has a feeling for the reason we defined a binary relation as we did. First we have an intuitive idea of a relation between ordered pairs of things—a relation such as "is married to" or "is less than". We observe that any one example of an "intuitive relation" (among ordered pairs) has associated with it the set of all those ordered pairs (x, y) such that x is related to y and that this set seems to be as explicitly and completely identifiable with the "intuitive relation" as anything we can think of. We then realize that the simplest thing to do is to call this set of ordered pairs the *relation*. The pleasant thought then comes to mind that perhaps we have mathematically defined a relation in terms of the concept of a set.

We hope, however, that the critical reader noticed that we did not give adequate attention to the concept of an ordered pair just before Definition 3.1. We did not rid that concept of an intuitive idea of one element being listed first or the intuitive idea of going from left to right. We thought it best to bypass this complication at that time. In the next paragraph we indicate how the concept of an ordered pair is made mathematically precise and is given in terms of sets alone.

Suppose $x \in X$ and $y \in Y$, where X and Y are sets. Then the set $\{\{x\}, \{x, y\}\}$ is called the *ordered pair with first coordinate x and second coordinate y* and is denoted by (x, y). (Note that the order in which things are listed is immaterial; $\{\{y, x\}, \{x\}\}$ is the same set as the last one written. Also note that the words "first coordinate" and "second coordinate" are just words used in naming the thing being defined. Finally (x, y) is just a notation, and the ordered pair denoted by (y, x) is the set $\{\{y\}, \{x, y\}\}$.) If $x = y$, then

$$(x, y) = \{\{x\}, \{x, x\}\} = \{\{x\}, \{x\}\} = \{\{x\}\} = (y, x).$$

Now that we have indicated how to define an ordered pair in terms of the concept "set", we would like to emphasize that:

Definition 3.2 is often adopted in order to give the concept "binary relation" in terms of the concept "set".

A similar statement in the third paragraph after 3.5 indicates the motivation for our particular definition of a function.

In this chapter we have not even given all of the items from set theory to be used later in this book. We have given what we consider to be a reasonable minimum of these items for the beginning of our study of topology. Other items will be mentioned when they are used in our main work.

References: Set Theory and Foundations

P. R. Halmos, *Naive Set Theory*. Princeton, N.J.: Van Nostrand, 1960.

E. Kamke, *Theory of Sets*. New York: Dover Publications, 1950.

R. L. Wilder, *Introduction to the Foundations of Mathematics*. New York: John Wiley and Sons, 1952.

References: Topology

S. S. Cairns, *Introductory Topology*. New York: Ronald Press, 1961.

D. W. Hall and G. L. Spencer, *Elementary Topology*. New York: John Wiley and Sons, 1955.

J. G. Hocking and G. S. Young, *Topology*. Reading, Mass.: Addison-Wesley, 1961.

J. L. Kelley, *General Topology*. Princeton, N.J.: Van Nostrand, 1955.

B. Mendelson, *Introduction to Topology*. Boston: Allyn and Bacon, 1962.

R. L. Moore, *Foundations of Point Set Theory*. New York: A. M. S. Colloquium Publication No. 13, 1932.

A. H. Wallace, *An Introduction to Algebraic Topology.* New York: Pergamon Press, 1957.

G. T. Whyburn, *Analytic Topology.* New York: A. M. S. Colloquium Publication No. 28, 1948.

R. L. Wilder, *Topology of Manifolds.* New York: A. M. S. Colloquium Publication No. 32, 1949.

2

Topological Spaces

1. Basic Concepts

Definition 1.1. Let X be a set. A collection $\mathcal{T}$ of subsets of X is called a *topology for* X iff

(a) the union of *each* subcollection of $\mathcal{T}$ is a member of $\mathcal{T}$ and

(b) the intersection of *each finite* subcollection of $\mathcal{T}$ is a member of $\mathcal{T}$ (where X is the underlying set).

Definition 1.2. Let $\mathcal{T}$ be a topology for a set X. Then the pair $(X, \mathcal{T})$ is called a *topological space*.

It should be verified that in each of the following examples the given family $\mathcal{T}$ is a topology.

Examples 1.3. (a) Let X be any set, and let $\mathcal{T}$ be the family of all subsets of X. Then $(X, \mathcal{T})$ is a topological space—a rather trivial one! This topology $\mathcal{T}$ is called the *discrete topology* for X.

(b) Let X be any set, and let $\mathcal{T} = \{\varnothing, X\}$. This (uninteresting) topology is called the *indiscrete topology* for X.

(c) Let $\mathcal{T}$ be the family of subsets of R (the reals) defined by: A subset K of R belongs to $\mathcal{T}$ iff

for each r in K there are real numbers a, b such that

$$a < r < b \text{ and } \{x:\ x \in R, a < x < b\} \subset K.$$

This topological space $(R, \mathcal{T})$ is a most important one!   Indeed, the notion of a topological space is an abstraction of some of the important properties of the system of real numbers.

(d) Let $X = \{a, b, c\}$ and let $\mathcal{T}$ be the family consisting of the following sets: $\varnothing$, $\{a\}$, $\{a, b\}$ and X.   This family $\mathcal{T}$ is a topology for X.   (Let the reader show that the family $\mathcal{F}$ consisting of the sets $\varnothing$, $\{a, b\}$, $\{a, c\}$ and X is not a topology.   Also show that the collection $\mathcal{C}$ consisting of the sets $\varnothing$, $\{a\}$, $\{b\}$, $\{a, c\}$ and X is not a topology for X.)

(e) Let X be any set and let $\mathcal{T}$ be the family of subsets of X defined as follows: A subset K of X belongs to $\mathcal{T}$ iff K is null or $X \sim K$ is finite. This topology is called the *finite complement topology*.

We see that there may be several different topologies for a given set X. In a discussion concerning a given topology $\mathcal{T}$ for a set X, it is customary to use the expressions "the topological space X" and "the space X" to mean $(X, \mathcal{T})$ without mentioning the topology $\mathcal{T}$ each time;   also these expressions are sometimes used to refer to the set X.   But extra care should be taken when confusion is likely.

The topology described in 1.3(c) for R is called the *usual topology for R*; and when we refer to "the space of real numbers" or "the space R" without mentioning a topology, it will be understood that the usual topology for R is the one under consideration.

If $(X, \mathcal{T})$ is a topological space, then the elements of X are usually called *points*.

Definition 1.4.   Let $(X, \mathcal{T})$ be a topological space.

(a) A subset G of X is said to be $\mathcal{T}$*-open* iff $G \in \mathcal{T}$.   (When the topology $\mathcal{T}$ is clearly understood, "$\mathcal{T}$-open" is shortened to "open".   This same practice is used for each concept defined here.   In the remaining definitions we omit the "$\mathcal{T}$" since $\mathcal{T}$ is clearly understood as the only topology mentioned here.)

(b) Suppose $p \in X$ and $U \subset X$.   Then U is called a *neighborhood of* p iff $p \in U$ and U is open.

(c) Suppose $K \subset X$ and $p \in X$. Then p is called an *accumulation point of K* (or a *limit point of K*) iff each neighborhood of p contains a point of K distinct from p. The set of all limit points of K is called the *derived set of K* and is denoted by K'.

(d) A subset H of X is said to be *closed* iff $X \sim H$ is open.

Exercises I.5

In 1–6 let $(X, \mathcal{T})$ be a topological space and prove the stated theorem.

1. The set $\varnothing$ is open.

2. The set X is open.

3. Each of the sets $\varnothing$ and X is also closed.

4. A subset G of X is open iff $X \sim G$ is closed.

5. A subset G of X is open iff for each point p in G, there is a neighborhood U_p of p such that $U_p \subset G$.

6. A subset H of X is closed iff $H' \subset H$.

7. In the space of real numbers R (with the usual topology), let $a, b \in R$ with $a < b$ and let

$$A = \{x: \quad x \in R, a < x < b\},$$

$$B = \{x: \quad x \in R, a \leq x \leq b\}$$

and

$$C = \{x: \quad x \in R, a \leq x < b\}.$$

(a) Which of the sets A, B and C are open?

(b) Specify the sets A', B' and C'.

(c) Which of the sets A, B and C are closed?

8. Suppose the set X in 1.3(e) is infinite, let A be any finite subset of X and let B be any infinite subset of X. Specify the sets A' and B' (relative to the finite complement topology).

9. Which subsets of X are closed (a) in the space of 1.3(a), (b) in the space of 1.3(b)?

The student should seriously attempt each of these exercises before reading the corresponding discussion.

Discussion of 1–3.   The union of the null subcollection of $\mathcal{T}$ is the null set $\varnothing$ [Ch 1, 2.3(a)].   Hence by 1.1(a), $\varnothing \in \mathcal{T}$, and so $\varnothing$ is open by 1.4(a). Since $X \sim X = \varnothing$, it follows from 1.4(d) that X is closed.

Since the null subcollection of $\mathcal{T}$ is a finite subcollection, it follows from 1.1(b) that the intersection of this subcollection, namely X [Ch 1, 2.3(b)], must belong to $\mathcal{T}$.   Hence X is open by 1.4(a).

Now since $X \sim \varnothing = X$, it follows from 1.4(d) that $\varnothing$ is closed.

Proof of 5.   First suppose G is open.   Then certainly for each p in G there is a neighborhood of p, namely G itself, which is a subset of G;   and the "only if" part of 5 is proved.

Next suppose that for each p in G there is a neighborhood of p which is contained in G.   Thus for each p in G select a neighborhood U_p of p such that $U_p \subset G$.   Clearly

$$\bigcup \{U_p: \quad p \in G\} \subset G$$

since each $U_p \subset G$.   Also

$$G \subset \bigcup \{U_p: \quad p \in G\}.$$

(Why?)   Hence

$$G = \bigcup \{U_p: \quad p \in G\}.$$

But each U_p is open (since it is a neighborhood of p);   and so the union, namely G, of these open sets must be open by 1.1(a), and 5 is proved.

Proof of 6.   Suppose H is closed.   Then $X \sim H$ is open and hence is a neighborhood of each of its points, which contains no point of H.   Therefore no point in $X \sim H$ is a limit point of H, i.e., $H' \subset H$.

Next suppose $H' \subset H$ and suppose $q \in X \sim H$.   Then $q \notin H'$ (since $H' \subset H$);   and so there is a neighborhood of q, say U, which contains no point of H, i.e., $U \subset X \sim H$.   Thus (by 5) $X \sim H$ is open, and hence H is closed.

In view of 1.4(a) we see that condition (a) in 1.1 may be stated as follows: The union of each collection of open sets is an open set.   Condition (b) in 1.1 may be stated: The intersection of each finite collection of open sets is an open set.

Let the reader use the DeMorgan formulae (Ch 1, 2.4) to prove the following theorem.

Theorem 1.6.   (a) In a topological space, the intersection of *each* collection of closed sets is a closed set.   (b) In a topological space, the union of *each finite* collection of closed sets is a closed set.

Remark 1.7.   Let $(X, \mathcal{T})$ be a topological space, and let A and B be subsets of X.   If $A \subset B$, then $A' \subset B'$.

Proof. Suppose $A \subset B$. If each neighborhood of a point p contains a point of A different from p, then surely each neighborhood of p contains a point of B different from p. Hence $A' \subset B'$.

Caution. Careless attempts at proving our next theorem are often fallacious, although a proof is easy. So the student should be cautious and doubly check his proof of this innocent looking little theorem.

Theorem I.8.   Let $(X, \mathscr{T})$ be a topological space, and let A and B be subsets of X. Then $(A \cup B)' = A' \cup B'$.

Proof. Since $A \subset A \cup B$, we have $A' \subset (A \cup B)'$ by 1.7. Similarly $B' \subset (A \cup B)'$. Therefore

(1) $$A' \cup B' \subset (A \cup B)'.$$

[To prove $(A \cup B)' \subset A' \cup B'$, we must show that if $p \in (A \cup B)'$, then $p \in A' \cup B'$; and to show this, we prove its contrapositive: if $p \notin A' \cup B'$ then $p \notin (A \cup B)'$.] Suppose $p \notin A'$ and $p \notin B'$. Then there exist neighborhoods U and V of p such that $U \cap A \sim \{p\} = \varnothing$ and $V \cap B \sim \{p\} = \varnothing$. Then the set $U \cap V$ is a neighborhood of p which contains no point of $A \cup B$ distinct from p, and so $p \notin (A \cup B)'$. Thus

(2) $$(A \cup B)' \subset A' \cup B'.$$

Now (1) and (2) implies $(A \cup B)' = A' \cup B'$, and 1.8 is proved.

By induction one can show that for each n in N

$$(A_1 \cup A_2 \cup \ldots \cup A_n)' = A_1' \cup A_2' \cup \ldots \cup A_n'$$

(where the notation is clear). However, the reader should give examples to show that the derived set of the union of an infinite collection of sets need not be equal to the union of the derived sets of the members of the collection and also to show that $(A \cap B)'$ need not be equal to $A' \cap B'$.

Two sets A and B are said to be *disjoint* (or A is said to be *disjoint from* B) iff $A \cap B = \varnothing$.

Theorem I.9.   Let $(X, \mathscr{Y})$ be a topological space, and let $A \subset X$. Then $A \cup A'$ is a closed set.

Proof. [To prove $A \cup A'$ is closed, we show $X \sim (A \cup A')$ is open; and to do this, we use 5 in 1.5.] Suppose $p \in X \sim (A \cup A')$. Then there exists a neighborhood U of p which is disjoint from A. Since U is a neighborhood of each of its points, no point in U is a limit point of A; so $U \subset X \sim (A \cup A')$. Therefore $X \sim (A \cup A')$ is open (1.5, 5).

Definition 1.10.   Let $A \subset X$, where $(X, \mathcal{T})$ is a topological space, let $\mathcal{C}$ be the collection of all closed subsets of X containing A and let $\mathcal{O}$ be the family of all open sets contained in A.

(a) The set $\bigcap \mathcal{C}$ is called the *closure of A* and is denoted by A^- or by $\bar{A}$.

(b) The set $\bigcup \mathcal{O}$ is called the *interior of A* and is denoted by A°.

Remark 1.11.   Let $A \subset X$, where $(X, \mathcal{T})$ is a topological space.

(a) A^- is a closed set [1.6(a)].

(b) $A \subset A^-$.

(c) A^- is the "smallest" closed set containing A in the sense that (1) A^- is a closed set containing A and (2) A^- is contained in each closed set which contains A (Ch 1, 2.5, no. 2).

(d) $A^- = A$ iff A is closed.

(e) $(A^-)^- = A^-$.

(f) $\varnothing^- = \varnothing$.

(g) A° is the "largest" open set contained in A.   State what we "naturally" mean by "largest" here.

(h) $A^\circ = A$ iff A is open.

Proof of (d). If $A^- = A$, then A is closed since A^- is closed by (a).
Now suppose A is closed.   Then by (c), $A^- \subset A$.   But by (b) $A \subset A^-$. Hence $A^- = A$.

Theorem 1.12.   If $A \subset X$ where $(X, \mathcal{T})$ is a topological space, then $A^- = A \cup A'$.

Proof. In view of 1.9, $A \cup A'$ is a closed set containing A.   So by 1.11(c), $A^- \subset A \cup A'$.
Now $A \subset A^-$.   So $A' \subset (A^-)' \subset A^-$ (1.7 and no. 6 in 1.5 since A^- is closed).   Hence $A \cup A' \subset A^-$.
Therefore $A^- = A \cup A'$.

Corollary 1.13.   In a topological space, a point $p \in A^-$ iff each neighborhood of p contains a point of A.

Corollary 1.14.   If A and B are subsets of a topological space (i.e., $A, B \subset X$ where $(X, \mathcal{T})$ is a topological space), then $(A \cup B)^- = A^- \cup B^-$.

We see that with each subset A of a topological space X, there is associated the set A^- called the closure of A. We have already observed that this association satisfies the conditions in the following theorem which we state for future reference.

Theorem I.15.   Let $(X, \mathcal{T})$ be a topological space.

(a) $\varnothing^- = \varnothing$.

(b) For each subset A of X, $A \subset A^-$.

(c) For each subset A of X, $(A^-)^- = A^-$.

(d) If $A, B \subset X$, then $(A \cup B)^- = A^- \cup B^-$.

Throughout our work we shall use E_2 to denote $R \times R$. For $p, q \in E_2$ we use $d(p, q)$ to denote the usual distance between p and q. Thus if $p = (a, b)$ and $q = (x, y)$, where $a, b, x, y \in R$, then

$$d(p, q) = [(x - a)^2 + (y - b)^2]^{1/2}.$$

For each p in E_2 and each positive r in R, the set

$$\{q: \quad q \in E_2 \quad \text{and} \quad d(p, q) < r\}$$

is temporarily called the *r-sphere with p as center* or the *r-sphere about p* and is denoted by $S_r(p)$. An r-sphere about p may be called a sphere about p or simply a sphere at times. (Some call $S_r(p)$ an "open sphere" and then call

$$\{q: \quad q \in E_2 \quad \text{and} \quad d(p, q) \leq r\}$$

a "closed sphere", but we do not wish to do this.) Some call $S_r(p)$ a *ball*.

Example I.16.   Let $\mathcal{T}$ be the family of subsets of E_2 defined as follows: A subset K of E_2 belongs to $\mathcal{T}$ iff K contains a sphere about each point in K. It is easy to see that $\mathcal{T}$ satisfies the conditions of 1.1, and so $\mathcal{T}$ is a topology for E_2. This topology will be referred to as the "usual topology for E_2" or the "usual topology for the Euclidean plane". When we refer to the space E_2 without mentioning a topology, we shall understand that the usual topology for E_2 is the one under consideration.

Definition I.17.   Let $(X, \mathcal{T})$ be a topological space, and let $A, B \subset X$.

(a) A is *dense in* B iff $B \subset (A \cap B)^-$. (It follows that A is dense in X iff $A^- = X$.)

(b) $(X, \mathcal{T})$ is *separable* iff there is a countable subset of X which is dense in X.

(c) $(X, \mathcal{T})$ is called a T_1 *space* iff for each $p \in X$, the set $\{p\}$ is a closed set.

(d) $(X, \mathcal{T})$ is called a T_2 *space* or a *Hausdorff space* iff $p, q \in X$ with $p \neq q$ implies there are disjoint neighborhoods U and V of p and q respectively (i.e., $U \cap V = \varnothing$).

Exercises 1.18

1. In the space of reals, let A, B and C be the sets given in 7 of 1.5, let D be the set of all rational real numbers, and let E be the set of all irrational numbers.

    (a) Specify the sets A^-, B^-, C^-, D^- and E^-.

    (b) What is the derived set of $A \cap D$?

    (c) Specify $(A \cap D)^-$, $(B \cap E)^-$ and $(R \sim B)^-$.

    (d) Specify $A°$, $B°$, $C°$, $D°$ and $E°$.

2. Give an example to show that if $G, H \subset R$, then $(G \cap H)^-$ may not be equal to $G^- \cap H^-$.

3. Let $p \in E_2$, let r be a positive real number, and let A be the set $S_r(p)$. What is the set A^-?

4. Let $A, B \subset X$ where X is a set. Prove $A \sim B = A \cap (X \sim B)$.

5. Let $A, B \subset X$ where $(X, \mathcal{T})$ is a topological space. Prove:

    (a) If A is open and B is closed, then $A \sim B$ is open.

    (b) If A is closed and B is open, then $A \sim B$ is closed.

    (c) If A and B are open, then $A \sim B$ may fail to be open.

    [Look for an example in E_2.]

6. Prove that if $(X, \mathcal{T})$ is a T_1 space, then each finite subset of X is closed. [Use 1.6(b) and 1.17(c).]

7. Let X be any set. What is the "smallest" family $\mathcal{F}$ of subsets of X such that $(X, \mathcal{F})$ is a T_1 space? [*Hint:* According to 6, each finite subset of X must be $\mathcal{F}$-closed.]

8. Prove that a topological space $(X, \mathcal{T})$ is a T_1 space iff $x, y \in X$ with $x \neq y$ implies there is a neighborhood U of x such that $y \notin U$.

9. Let $(X, \mathcal{T})$ be a T_1 space. Prove that a point p of X is a limit point of a subset A of X iff each neighborhood of p contains infinitely many points of A (i.e., iff for each neighborhood U of p, the set $U \cap A$ is infinite).

10. Prove that if $A \subset X$, where $(X, \mathcal{T})$ is a T_1 space, then A' is a closed set. [See 6 in 1.5 and use 9 above to show $(A')' \subset A'$.]

11. Prove that each T_2 space is a T_1 space.

12. Which spaces in 1.3 and 1.16 are T_2 spaces?

13. Give an example of a topological space which is (a) not a T_1 space, (b) a T_1 space but not a T_2 space. [Such examples are found in 1.3.]

14. (a) Give an example of a collection of open subsets of R whose intersection is not open.

    (b) Give an example of a collection of closed subsets of R whose union is not closed.

15. Which spaces in 1.3 and 1.16 are separable?

Proof of 8. First suppose $(X, \mathcal{T})$ is a T_1 space, and suppose $x, y \in X$ with $x \neq y$. By hypothesis $\{y\}$ is closed, and so $X \sim \{y\}$ is clearly a neighborhood of x which does not contain y.

Now suppose that for each x, y in X with $x \neq y$, there is a neighborhood U of x such that $y \notin U$. To show the space is T_1, suppose $p \in X$. [We want to show $\{p\}$ is closed by using 5 of 1.5 to show $X \sim \{p\}$ is open.] Now suppose $q \in X \sim \{p\}$. Then $q \neq p$, and by hypothesis there is a neighborhood U of q such that $U \subset X \sim \{p\}$. Therefore by 5 in 1.5, $X \sim \{p\}$ is open. Hence $\{p\}$ is closed and $(X, \mathcal{T})$ is a T_1 space.

Proof of 9. Certainly, if each neighborhood of p contains infinitely many points of A, then each neighborhood of p contains a point of A different from p, and so $p \in A'$.

To prove the other half, suppose there is a neighborhood U of p such that $U \cap A$ is finite. Let $W = U \cap A \sim \{p\}$. Then W is finite, and so W is closed by 6 (since our space X is T_1). Thus, by 5(a), $U \sim W$ is open. It follows that $U \sim W$ is a neighborhood of p which contains no point of A different from p. We have shown that if there is a neighborhood U of p such that $U \cap A$ is finite, then $p \notin A'$. This means that if $p \in A'$ (in a T_1 space), then each neighborhood of p must contain infinitely many points of A.

Proof of 10. Suppose $p \in (A')'$. (We want to show $p \in A'$.) Let U be any neighborhood of p. Then U must contain a point q in A' (since p is a limit point of A'). Now since U is a neighborhood of q and $q \in A'$, it follows from 9 that U contains infinitely many points of A. Hence by 9, $p \in A'$. We have shown that $(A')' \subset A'$. Therefore in a T_1 space, A' is closed.

Discussion of 13.   (a) The space in 1.3(d) is not a T_1 space; for $\{b\}$ is not closed (since $\{a, c\}$ is not open).   The space in 1.3(b) is not T_1 in case X contains more than one point.

(b) Let X be an *infinite* set with the finite complement topology of 1.3(e). In this space for each p in X, the set $X \sim \{p\}$ is surely open so that $\{p\}$ is closed and the space is T_1.   Now let $x, y \in X$ with $x \neq y$, and let U and V be *any* neighborhoods of x and y respectively.   Then $X \sim U$ must be finite while V must be infinite, so that V cannot be contained in $X \sim U$; i.e., some point of V must be in U.   Since U and V are arbitrary neighborhoods of x and y, it follows that there do not exist disjoint neighborhoods of x and y.   Thus this space is not T_2.

Discussion of 14.   Let $a, b \in R$ with $a < b$.   We call $\{x: \ a < x < b\}$ the open interval from a to b or the open interval with end points a and b (though, of course, a and b do not belong to this set).   The set $\{x: \ a \leq x \leq b\}$ is called the closed interval with end points a and b (or from a to b). Fortunately, relative to the usual topology for R, an open interval is an open set and a closed interval is a closed set.

(a) For each n in N, let A_n be the open interval from $-1/n$ to $1 + 1/n$. We see that $\bigcap \{A_n: \ n \in N\} = \{x: \ 0 \leq x \leq 1\}$, which is not open.

(b) For each n in N, let A_n be the closed interval from $1/n$ to $3 - 1/n$. Here

$$\bigcup \{A_n: \ n \in N\} = \{x: \ 0 < x < 3\},$$

which is not closed.

Answer to 7.   Let $\mathscr{F}$ be the finite complement topology for X.   Clearly $\mathscr{F}$ is a "T_1 topology" for X.   Now let $\mathscr{T}$ be *any* T_1 topology for X, and let $K \in \mathscr{F}$.   If $K = \varnothing$, then $K \in \mathscr{T}$.   But if $K \neq \varnothing$, then $X \sim K$ is finite; and by 6, $X \sim K$ is $\mathscr{T}$-closed.   Hence K is $\mathscr{T}$-open, i.e., $K \in \mathscr{T}$.   We have shown that $\mathscr{F} \subset \mathscr{T}$.   Thus $\mathscr{F}$ is the smallest T_1 topology for X.

2. Convergence of a Sequence

Definition 2.1.   A mapping of N into a set X is called a *sequence* or a *sequence in* X.

When a mapping is a sequence, we often denote this mapping by S, and for each n in N we may denote the image of n under S by $S(n)$ or more often by S_n.

Definition 2.2.   Let S be a sequence in a set X and let $A \subset X$.

(a) S is said to be *in* A iff for each n in N, $S_n \in A$.

(b) S is said to be *eventually in* A iff there is some m in N such that $S_n \in A$ for each n in N with $n \geq m$.

(c) Let $\mathscr{T}$ be a topology for X and let $p \in X$. Then S is said to $\mathscr{T}$-*converge* (or *converge*) *to* p iff S is eventually in each neighborhood of p.

Exercises 2.3

1. Prove that the sequence $S\colon N \longrightarrow R$ defined by $S_n = 1/n$ converges to 0.

2. (a) Let $(X, \mathscr{T})$ be a topological space, let $c \in X$, and let S be a sequence in X which is eventually in $\{c\}$. Show that S converges to c. Could this sequence converge to some other point in X? Could this sequence converge to a point different from c if $(X, \mathscr{T})$ is a T_1 space?

   (b) What sequences in the space of 1.3(a) converge to what points?

   (c) Prove that in a T_2 space a sequence can converge to at most one point.

   (d) Give an example of a sequence which converges to at least two distinct points.

   (e) What sequences in the space of 1.3(b) converge to what points? [Reconsider (d).]

3. Let $(X, \mathscr{T})$ be a topological space, let $A \subset X$, and let $p \in X$.

   (a) Prove that if there is a sequence S in $A \sim \{p\}$ which converges to p, then $p \in A'$.

   (b) Show that the converse of the proposition in (a) is not true.

   (c) Prove that if there is a sequence S in A which converges to p, then $p \in A^-$. (Use 1.13.)

Proof of 1. Let U be *any* neighborhood of 0. Then (by definition of the usual topology for R in 1.3(c)) there are real numbers a, b in R with $a < 0 < b$ such that the open interval V from a to b is a subset of U. Now (from properties of R which we accept) there is an m in N such that $0 < 1/n < b$ if $n \geq m$. So for each n in N with $n \geq m$, we have $S_n = 1/n \in V \subset U$. Hence S is eventually in the arbitrary neighborhood U of 0. Thus S converges to 0.

Proof of 2(c). Suppose p and q are distinct points in a T_2 space, and let U and V be disjoint neighborhoods of p and q respectively. Now a sequence cannot be eventually in each of these disjoint sets. (For if S were eventually in U and eventually in V, there would be numbers m and k in N such that $S_n \in U$ if $n \geq m$ and $S_n \in V$ if $n \geq k$; but there is an i in N with $i \geq m$ and $i \geq k$ so that $S_i \in U$ and $S_i \in V$, which is impossible since $U \cap V = \emptyset$.) Hence in a T_2 space a sequence cannot converge to two distinct points.

Proof of 3(a) and (b).   (a) To show $p \in A'$, let U be *any* neighborhood of p. Then (since S converges to p) there is an m in N such that $S_n \in U$ if $n \geq m$. So

$$S_m \in U \quad \text{and} \quad S_m \in A \sim \{p\} \quad \text{(since } S \text{ is in } A \sim \{p\}).$$

Hence $p \in A'$.

(b) Let X be an uncountable set, and let $\mathcal{T}$ be the family of subsets of X defined as follows: A subset G of X belongs to $\mathcal{T}$ iff $G = \emptyset$ or $X \sim G$ is countable. (Let the reader show that $\mathcal{T}$ is a topology for X.) (What kind of sequences may converge to a point in this space?) Let $p \in X$, and let $A = X \sim \{p\}$. Clearly $p \in A'$. But no sequence in A can converge to p. For let S be *any* sequence in A, and let $H = \{x: \ x = S_n \text{ for } n \text{ in } N\}$. Now H is countable, and so $X \sim H$ is a neighborhood of p. But S is "never in" $X \sim H$. Thus S does not converge to p.

The converse of the proposition in 3(a) is true in "first countable" spaces, which we now define.

Definition 2.4.   Let $(X, \mathcal{T})$ be a topological space, and let $\mathcal{C}$ be a collection of neighborhoods of a point p in X.

(a) $\mathcal{C}$ is called a *local base at p* (or a *base for the neighborhood system at p*) iff each neighborhood of p contains a member of $\mathcal{C}$.

(b) The space $(X, \mathcal{T})$ is said to be *first countable* (or *to satisfy the first axiom of countability*) iff there is a countable local base at each point of X.

Remark 2.5.   If $\{U_1, U_2, U_3, \ldots\}$ is a countable local base at a point p in a space, then there is a monotone decreasing collection $\{V_1, V_2, V_3, \ldots\}$ of neighborhoods of p which is a local base at p.

By "monotone decreasing" we mean that $V_{n+1} \subset V_n$ for each n in N. To prove 2.5 let $V_n = U_1 \cap U_2 \cap \ldots \cap U_n$ for each n in N (where it is understood that $V_1 = U_1$).

Theorem 2.6.   (a) In a first countable space, $p \in A'$ iff there is a sequence in $A \sim \{p\}$ which converges to p.

(b) In a first countable space, $p \in A^-$ iff there is a sequence in A which converges to p.

Proof of (a). The "if" part is covered by 3(a) in 2.3. So suppose $p \in A'$. In view of 2.5, let $\{V_1, V_2, V_3, \ldots\}$ be a monotone decreasing countable local base at p. Since $p \in A'$, for each n in N, we may select a point S_n in $V_n \cap (A \sim \{p\})$. We leave it to the reader to show that the sequence thus obtained converges to p.

The following simple remark will be useful in the future.

Remark 2.7.   Let C be a local base at a point p in a space X.

(a) $p \in A'$ (where $A \subset X$) iff each V in C contains a point of $A \sim \{p\}$.

(b) $p \in A^-$ (where $A \subset X$) iff each V in C contains a point of A.   (See 1.13.)

(c) A sequence S in X converges to p iff S is eventually in each member of C.

Exercises 2.8

1. What sequences in the space of 1.3(e) converge to what points?

2. Let $(X, \mathcal{T})$ be a T_1 space, and let C be a local base at a point p in X. Prove $\bigcap C = \{p\}$.

3. Bases and Subbases for a Topology

Definition 3.1.   Let $\mathcal{B}$ be a family of subsets of a set X. Then the family of all sets, each of which is the union of a subfamily of $\mathcal{B}$, is called the family *generated by* $\mathcal{B}$ and is denoted by $\mathcal{B}^*$. We also say $\mathcal{B}$ *generates* $\mathcal{B}^*$.

Thus if $\mathcal{B}$ is a family of sets, then a set A belongs to $\mathcal{B}^*$ iff A is the union of a collection of members of $\mathcal{B}$. We see that $\mathcal{B}$ is a subfamily of $\mathcal{B}^*$; for if $B \in \mathcal{B}$, then B is the union of the family $\{B\}$ (which is a subfamily of $\mathcal{B}$).

Remark 3.2.   Let $\mathcal{B}$ be a family of sets, and let A be a set. Then $A \in \mathcal{B}^*$ iff

for each p in A there is a B in $\mathcal{B}$ such that $p \in B$ and $B \subset A$.

Theorem 3.3.   If $\mathscr{B}$ and $\mathscr{C}$ are families of sets, then $\mathscr{B}^* = \mathscr{C}^*$ iff

(a) for each C in $\mathscr{C}$ and each p in C, there is a B in $\mathscr{B}$ such that $p \in B$ and $B \subset C$, and

(b) for each B in $\mathscr{B}$ and each p in B, there is a C in $\mathscr{C}$ such that $p \in C$ and $C \subset B$.

Proof. Suppose (a) and (b) hold, and let $A \in \mathscr{B}^*$. Suppose $p \in A$. By 3.2, there is a B in $\mathscr{B}$ such that $p \in B$ and $B \subset A$. By hypothesis (b), there is a C in $\mathscr{C}$ such that $p \in C$ and $C \subset B$. Hence $C \subset A$, and therefore, by 3.2, $A \in \mathscr{C}^*$. Thus $\mathscr{B}^* \subset \mathscr{C}^*$. Similarly $\mathscr{C}^* \subset \mathscr{B}^*$, and so $\mathscr{B}^* = \mathscr{C}^*$.

Conversely, suppose $\mathscr{B}^* = \mathscr{C}^*$, and suppose $B \in \mathscr{B}$. Then (as observed before 3.2) $B \in \mathscr{B}^*$ ($= \mathscr{C}^*$ by hypothesis), and so $B \in \mathscr{C}^*$. Therefore by 3.2 (applied to $\mathscr{C}^*$), condition (b) holds. Similarly (a) holds, and 3.3 is proved.

Exercises 3.4

1. Let $\mathscr{B}$ be the family of all open intervals in R. (See discussion of 14 in 1.18 for meaning of open interval in R.) What is the family $\mathscr{B}^*$ in this case?

2. Let $\mathscr{C}$ be the family of all open intervals in R with both end points rational. Is $\mathscr{C}^*$ equal to the $\mathscr{B}^*$ of exercise 1?

Pleasantly enough, the answer to exercise 1 is that $\mathscr{B}^* = \mathscr{T}$, where $\mathscr{T}$ is the usual topology for R. To see this, compare the criterion in 1.3(c) (which determines whether or not a set belongs to $\mathscr{T}$) with the criterion in 3.2 (which determines whether or not a set belongs to $\mathscr{B}^*$).

But (as will be clear a little later) an even more pleasant result is contained in the answer to exercise 2; namely, $\mathscr{C}^* = \mathscr{B}^*$. To see this, we use 3.3.

Since $\mathscr{C} \subset \mathscr{B}$, clearly (a) in 3.3 holds. Also, if $p \in B$, where B is an open interval in R, then there is an open interval C with rational end points such that $p \in C$ and $C \subset B$. Hence (b) in 3.3 holds. Therefore by 3.3, $\mathscr{C}^* = \mathscr{B}^*$.

Let $X = \{1, 2, 3, 4\}$ and let $\mathscr{B}$ be the family of sets consisting of $\{1, 2\}$, $\{1, 4\}$ and $\{2, 3\}$. Then $\mathscr{B}^*$ consists of

$$\varnothing, \quad \{1, 2\}, \quad \{1, 4\}, \quad \{2, 3\}, \quad \{1, 2, 4\}, \quad \{1, 2, 3\} \quad \text{and } X.$$

We see that $\mathscr{B}^*$ is not a topology (since $\{1, 2\} \cap \{2, 3\} = \{2\}$, but $\{2\} \notin \mathscr{B}^*$).

Thus if $\mathscr{B}$ is a family of subsets of a set X, then $\mathscr{B}^*$ may or may not be a topology for X. The next theorem tells us when $\mathscr{B}$ does generate a topology.

Theorem 3.5. Let $\mathscr{B}$ be a collection of subsets of a set X. Then $\mathscr{B}^*$ is a topology for X iff

(a) $\bigcup \mathscr{B} = X$, and

(b) for each A, B in $\mathscr{B}$ and each p in $A \cap B$, there is a C in $\mathscr{B}$ such that $p \in C$ and $C \subset A \cap B$.

Proof. First, suppose $\mathscr{B}^*$ is a topology for X. Then X is $\mathscr{B}^*$-open, i.e., $X \in \mathscr{B}^*$, and so X is the union of some subfamily of $\mathscr{B}$; hence $\bigcup \mathscr{B}$ is surely equal to X, and (a) is proved. Since $\mathscr{B} \subset \mathscr{B}^*$, members A and B of $\mathscr{B}$ are open; hence $A \cap B$ is open, so $A \cap B \in \mathscr{B}^*$, and (b) follows from 3.2.

Now suppose (a) and (b) of 3.5 hold. The union of members of $\mathscr{B}^*$ is itself a union of members of $\mathscr{B}$ and is therefore a member of $\mathscr{B}^*$; thus (a) in 1.1 is satisfied. Let $U, V \in \mathscr{B}^*$ and suppose $p \in U \cap V$. Then, by 3.2, there are members A and B of $\mathscr{B}$ such that $p \in A \subset U$ and $p \in B \subset V$. By hypothesis (b), there is a C in $\mathscr{B}$ such that

$$p \in C \subset A \cap B \subset U \cap V.$$

Hence, by 3.2, $U \cap V \in \mathscr{B}^*$. By induction, the intersection of any non-void finite subfamily of $\mathscr{B}^*$ is a member of $\mathscr{B}^*$. But the intersection of the null subcollection of $\mathscr{B}^*$, namely X, is a member of $\mathscr{B}^*$ by hypothesis (a). Hence (b) in 1.1 is satisfied, and $\mathscr{B}^*$ is a topology for X.

Clearly the family $\mathscr{B}$ of all open intervals in R satisfies (a) and (b) in 3.5. Thus 3.5 implies that $\mathscr{B}^*$ is a topology for R. But we already know that $\mathscr{B}^*$ is the family $\mathscr{T}$ in 1.3(c). Thus 3.5 offers a convenient way to prove that the family $\mathscr{T}$ in 1.3(c) is a topology.

Definition 3.6. Let $(X, \mathscr{T})$ be a topological space.

(a) A family $\mathscr{B}$ of sets is called a *base for* $\mathscr{T}$ iff $\mathscr{B}^* = \mathscr{T}$.

(b) The space is said to be *second countable* (or *to satisfy the second axiom of countability*) iff there is a countable base for $\mathscr{T}$.

We have already mentioned in 3.4 two different bases for the usual topology for R. So a topology may have several bases.

Theorem 3.7. If a space $(X, \mathscr{T})$ is second countable, then it is separable.

Proof. (See 1.17(b).) Let $\mathscr{B}$ be a countable base for $\mathscr{T}$. Select a point from each non-void member of $\mathscr{B}$, thus obtaining a countable set A. Suppose there were a point p in $X \sim A^-$. Then since $X \sim A^-$ is open, there is (by 3.2) a B in $\mathcal{B}$ such that $p \in B \subset X \sim A^-$.   But from our construction of A, A contains a point of B; and $B \subset X \sim A^-$ is impossible.   Our supposition that there is a p in $X \sim A^-$ led to this impossibility.   So we conclude that $X \sim A^- = \varnothing$, and hence $A^- = X$.   Thus the space is separable.

A family $\mathcal{C}$ of sets is called a *cover for a set A* iff $A \subset \bigcup \mathcal{C}$;   we also say $\mathcal{C}$ *covers A*.   A cover $\mathcal{C}$ for A is called an *open cover for A* iff each member of $\mathcal{C}$ is an open set.   If $\mathcal{C}$ is a cover for A, then a subfamily $\mathcal{D}$ of $\mathcal{C}$ is called a *subcover (of $\mathcal{C}$) for A* iff $\mathcal{D}$ covers A.

Theorem 3.8 (Lindelöf).   Let $(X, \mathcal{T})$ be a second countable space, and let $A \subset X$.   Then each open cover for A has a countable subcover for A.

Proof.   Let $\mathcal{C}$ be an open cover for A, and let $\mathcal{B}$ be a countable base for $\mathcal{T}$.   Let $\mathcal{F}$ be the subfamily of $\mathcal{B}$ defined as follows: A member B of $\mathcal{B}$ belongs to $\mathcal{F}$ iff there is a G in $\mathcal{C}$ such that $B \subset G$.   Clearly

$$(1) \qquad\qquad \bigcup \mathcal{F} = \bigcup \mathcal{C} \supset A$$

(since each G in $\mathcal{C}$ is the union of some members of $\mathcal{F}$).   But $\mathcal{F}$ is countable since it is a subfamily of the countable base $\mathcal{B}$.   Now for each B in $\mathcal{F}$, select a member G_B in $\mathcal{C}$ such that $B \subset G_B$—thus obtaining a countable subfamily $\mathcal{D}$ of $\mathcal{C}$.   By (1), $\mathcal{F}$ covers A, and so $\mathcal{D}$ surely covers A (since each member of $\mathcal{F}$ is a subset of some member of $\mathcal{D}$).   Thus $\mathcal{D}$ is the required countable subcover for A.

A space $(X, \mathcal{T})$ is called a *Lindelöf space* iff each open cover for X has a countable subcover for X.   By taking $A = X$ in 3.8, we obtain the corollary that each second countable space is a Lindelöf space.

Exercises 3.9

1.   Prove that if A is a closed subset of a Lindelöf space X, then each open cover for A has a countable subcover for A.

2.   Let $\mathcal{S}$ be a collection of subsets of an underlying set X, and let $\mathcal{B}$ be the family of all finite intersections of members of $\mathcal{S}$.   (By a "finite intersection of members of $\mathcal{S}$" we mean the intersection of a finite subfamily of $\mathcal{S}$.)   Prove that $\mathcal{B}$ is a base for a topology for X (i.e., prove $\mathcal{B}^*$ is a topology for X).

3.   Let $\mathcal{T}$ be a topology for a set X.   What is the family $\mathcal{T}^*$?   Is $\mathcal{T}$ a base for $\mathcal{T}$?

4. Which of the spaces in 1.3 and 1.16 are second countable? Which of these spaces are separable but not second countable? (See 15 in 1.18.)

5. (a) Let $\mathscr{B}$ be a base for a topology for a set X, let $p \in X$, and let $\mathscr{C}$ be the collection of all members of $\mathscr{B}$ which contain p. Prove that $\mathscr{C}$ is a local base at p.

(b) Prove each second countable space is first countable.

(c) Give an example of a first countable space which is not second countable.

Proof of 2. (We use 3.5.) The underlying set X belongs to $\mathscr{B}$ (since X is the intersection of a finite subcollection of $\mathscr{S}$, namely the null subcollection). Hence (a) in 3.5 follows. Now let $A, B \in \mathscr{B}$. Then A is a finite intersection of members of $\mathscr{S}$; so is B. Hence $A \cap B$ is a finite intersection of members of $\mathscr{S}$, and so $A \cap B \in \mathscr{B}$. Therefore for each p in $A \cap B$ there is a member, namely $A \cap B$, of $\mathscr{B}$ which contains p and is contained in $A \cap B$. Thus (b) in 3.5 holds, and $\mathscr{B}^*$ is a topology for X.

Definition 3.10. Let $(X, \mathscr{T})$ be a topological space. A family $\mathscr{S}$ of subsets of X is called a *subbase for* $\mathscr{T}$ iff the family of all finite intersections of members of $\mathscr{S}$ generates $\mathscr{T}$.

In view of 2 in 3.9, each family $\mathscr{S}$ of subsets of a set X is a subbase for some topology $\mathscr{T}$ for X. It is clear that this topology $\mathscr{T}$ is the smallest topology for X which contains $\mathscr{S}$ as a subfamily.

For each real number r, we call the set $\{x: \ x < r\}$ an *open left ray* in R and the set $\{x: \ x > r\}$ an *open right ray* in R. It is easy to see that the family of all open rays in R is a subbase for the usual topology for R.

Discussion of 4. If the set X in 1.3(a) is uncountable, this space is not separable, hence cannot be second countable by 3.7. But in case X is a countable set, the family $\mathscr{B}$ of all sets of the form $\{p\}$ for p in X is clearly a countable base for the discrete topology. (Some writers call $\{p\}$ a *singleton set.*)

Of course the whole family $\mathscr{T}$ in 1.3(b) is countable and hence is a countable base for itself.

The answer to 2 in 3.4 shows that R (with the usual topology) is second countable.

It is easy to see that the family of all spheres in E_2 with rational radii and rational centers is a base for the usual topology for E_2 given in 1.16. Exercise 3 in 4.13 of Ch 1 was provided for our use at this time.

Suppose there is a countable base $\mathscr{B}$ for the family $\mathscr{T}$ in 1.3(e), and suppose $p \in X$. Then the family $\mathscr{C}$ of all members of $\mathscr{B}$ which contain p is countable. From 2 in 2.8 and 5(a) in 3.9, we have $\bigcap \mathcal{C} = \{p\}$. By a DeMorgan formula,

$$\bigcup \{X \sim B: \quad B \in \mathcal{C}\} = X \sim \{p\}.$$

From 4.12 in Ch 1, the union on the left is countable. So $X \sim \{p\}$ is countable; hence X is countable. We have shown that if the space in 1.3(e) is second countable, then X is a countable set. It remains to be shown that if X is countable, then the space in 1.3(e) is, in fact, second countable. To do this, we need the following result (postponed from Ch 1):

(α)   The family of all finite subsets of N is countable.

Proof. Let $\mathcal{F}$ be the family of all non-void finite subsets of N. Define a mapping $f: \mathcal{F} \longrightarrow N$ such that for each $A = \{n, m, \ldots, k\}$ in $\mathcal{F}$ labeled so that $n < m < \ldots < k$,

$$f(A) = 2^n 3^m \ldots p^k, \quad \text{where } 2, 3, \ldots, p \text{ are successive primes.}$$

Thus we have defined a one-to-one mapping of $\mathcal{F}$ into N. By 3 in 4.9 of Ch 1, $\mathcal{F}$ is countable. Hence $\mathcal{F} \cup \{\varnothing\}$ (i.e., the family of all finite subsets of N) is countable, and (α) is proved.

From (α) we have immediately:

(β)   If X is a countable set, then the family of all finite subsets of X is countable.

From (β) we now have: If X is countable, then the family $\mathcal{T}$ in 1.3(e) is countable and hence is a countable base for itself.

Thus the space in 1.3(e) is second countable iff X is countable. But we already know (if we have properly settled 15 in 1.18) that this space is separable no matter what the set X may be. This space with X uncountable is the only separable space among our listed examples which does not satisfy the second axiom of countability.

4.   Subspaces and Separated Sets

Definition 4.1.   Let $Y \subset X$, where $(X, \mathcal{T})$ is a topological space. Let $\mathcal{F}$ be the family of sets defined as follows: A set W belongs to $\mathcal{F}$ iff there is a member U in $\mathcal{T}$ such that $W = Y \cap U$. The family $\mathcal{F}$ is called *the relativization of $\mathcal{T}$ to Y.*

Let the reader show that $\mathcal{F}$ is a topology for Y. Because of the distributive property of intersection over unions, it is easy to see that if $\mathcal{B}$ is a base for $\mathcal{T}$, then the family of all intersections of members of $\mathcal{B}$ with Y is a base for $\mathcal{F}$.

Definition 4.2.   The family $\mathscr{F}$ in 4.1 is called the *relative topology for* Y, and $(Y, \mathscr{F})$ is called a *subspace of* $(X, \mathscr{T})$.

Theorem 4.3.   If $(Y, \mathscr{F})$ is a subspace of $(X, \mathscr{T})$ and $A \subset Y$, then a point y in Y is an $\mathscr{F}$-limit point of A iff y is a $\mathscr{T}$-limit point of A.

Proof. Since each $\mathscr{F}$-neighborhood of y is the intersection of Y and a $\mathscr{T}$-neighborhood of y, it follows that each $\mathscr{F}$-neighborhood of y contains a point of $A \sim \{y\}$ iff each $\mathscr{T}$-neighborhood of y contains a point of $A \sim \{y\}$.

Corollary 4.4.   The $\mathscr{F}$-closure of the set A in 4.3 is the intersection of Y and the $\mathscr{T}$-closure of A.

Proof

$$A^{-(\mathscr{F})} = A \cup A'^{(\mathscr{F})}$$
$$= A \cup [A'^{(\mathscr{T})} \cap Y] \qquad \text{(by 4.3)}$$
$$= [A \cap Y] \cup [A'^{(\mathscr{T})} \cap Y] \qquad (\text{since } A \subset Y)$$
$$= [A \cup A'^{(\mathscr{T})}] \cap Y \qquad \text{(distributivity)}$$
$$= A^{-(\mathscr{T})} \cap Y$$

where $A^{-(\mathscr{F})}$ denotes the $\mathscr{F}$-closure of A and the other notation is interpreted similarly.

Definition 4.5.   Let $Y \subset X$, where $(X, \mathscr{T})$ is a topological space. A subset A of Y is said to be *open* (*closed*) *in* Y iff A is $\mathscr{F}$-open ($\mathscr{F}$-closed) respectively where $\mathscr{F}$ is the relative topology for Y.

Exercises 4.6

Let $(Y, \mathscr{F})$ be a subspace of a space $(X, \mathscr{T})$.

1. Prove: (a) If A is open in Y and Y is open in X, then A is open in X.
   (b) If A is closed in Y, then there is a $\mathscr{T}$-closed set H in X such that $A = H \cap Y$.
   (c) If A is closed in Y and Y is closed in X, then A is closed in X.

2. Is the converse of 1(b) true?

3. By taking $(X, \mathscr{T})$ to be the space of reals, give examples to show that A may be open (closed) in Y without being open (closed) in X, in case Y is not open (closed) in X.

4. We say that a given property of a space is *hereditary* iff: $(X, \mathcal{T})$ has the property implies $(Y, \mathcal{F})$ has the property, for each space $(X, \mathcal{T})$. Which of the following are hereditary: the property of being T_1, T_2, first countable, second countable, separable, Lindelöf?

Proof of 1(b). Suppose A is closed in Y. Then $A = A^{-(\mathcal{F})} = A^{-(\mathcal{T})} \cap Y$. So H may be taken as $A^{-(\mathcal{F})}$.

Definition 4.7.   Two subsets A and B of a space X are said to be *separated* iff $A \neq \emptyset$, $B \neq \emptyset$ and $A \cap B^- = \emptyset = A^- \cap B$.

Suppose A and B are disjoint subsets of X where $(X, \mathcal{T})$ is a space. Then $A \cap B^- = \emptyset$ iff A contains no $\mathcal{T}$-limit point of B, i.e., iff B contains all of its $\mathcal{T}$-limit points which are in $A \cup B$; but (in view of 4.3) this is true iff B is closed in the subspace $A \cup B$. Similarly (with A and B disjoint) $A^- \cap B = \emptyset$ iff A is closed in $A \cup B$. Part (a) of the next remark is now clear.

Remark 4.8.   Let A and B be non-void disjoint subsets of a space. Then:

(a) A and B are separated iff each is closed in the subspace $A \cup B$.

(b) A and B are separated iff each is open in their union.

(c) A and B are separated iff A is both open and closed in $A \cup B$.

Parts (b) and (c) follow from (a) since, by hypothesis, A and B are disjoint and so they are complementary sets in the subspace $A \cup B$.

Exercises 4.9

1. Let A and B be separated subsets of a space, and let C and D be non-void sets such that $C \subset A$ and $D \subset B$. Prove that C and D are separated.

2. Let A be the open interval from 0 to 1 in R, let B be the open interval from 1 to 2, and let C be the closed interval from 1 to 2.
    (a) Are A and B separated?
    (b) Are A and C separated?

5. Connected Sets

Definition 5.1.   A subset K of a space is *connected* iff K is not the union of two separated sets.

In particular, a space X is connected iff X is not the union of two separated sets.

Definition 5.2.   A subset Y of a set Z is called a *proper subset* of Z iff $Y \neq \emptyset$ and $Y \neq Z$.

(Many writers omit the condition that $Y \neq \emptyset$ in 5.2.   But we find our terminology convenient for our purposes.   We deliberately postponed this definition from Ch 1 for several reasons.)

Part (c) of 4.8 gives us the following result.

Remark 5.3.   A subset Y of a space is connected iff Y contains no proper subset which is both open and closed in Y.

The null subset of a space is not the union of two separated sets (see 4.7), and hence is connected.   A set consisting of a single point contains no proper subset.   Hence, by 5.3, such a set is connected.

Exercises 5.4

1. Which of the spaces in (a), (b), (d) and (e) of 1.3 are connected?
    [For X infinite in (e), recall 8 in 1.5.]

2. Let A and B be separated subsets of a space, and let C be a connected subset of $A \cup B$.   Prove that $C \subset A$ or $C \subset B$.   (Use 1 in 4.9.)

Theorem 5.5.   Let C be a connected set, and let D be a set such that $C \subset D \subset C^-$.   Then D is connected.

Proof.   Suppose D were not connected.   Then

$$C \subset D = A \cup B \subset C^-,$$

where A and B are separated.   By 2 of 5.4, $C \subset A$ or $C \subset B$.   Suppose the labeling chosen so that $C \subset A$.   It follows that B contains a limit point of C and hence (by 1.7) a limit point of A.   But this is a contradiction since A and B were separated.   Hence D must be connected.

By taking $D = C^-$ in 5.5 ($C \subset C^- \subset C^-$), we obtain:

Corollary 5.6.   If C is connected, then C^- is connected.

Definition 5.7.   A space X is said to be *locally connected* iff for each p in X and each neighborhood U of p there is a connected neighborhood V of p such that $V \subset U$.

Clearly a space is locally connected iff the family of all open connected sets in the space is a base for the topology.

Exercises 5.8

1. Let C be a collection of connected subsets of a space. Prove that if no two members of C are separated, then $\bigcup C$ is connected.

2. Prove that a space X is locally connected iff for each $p \in X$ and each neighborhood U of p, the union of all connected subsets of U which contain p is an open connected set.

3. Let C be a connected subset of a connected set K. If $K \sim C = A \cup B$, where A and B are separated, then $A \cup C$ is connected. (Of course $B \cup C$ is also connected.)

4. Let $Z \subset Y \subset X$, where $(X, \mathcal{T})$ is a topological space, and let $A \subset Z$.

    (a) Prove: If A is open in Y, then A is open in Z. [Here we refer to Z as a subspace of X, not as a subspace of the subspace Y— although this makes no difference in view of (b).]

    (b) Let $\mathcal{F}_1$ be the relativization of $\mathcal{T}$ to Z, and let $\mathcal{F}_2$ be the relativization of $\mathcal{F}$ to Z, where $\mathcal{F}$ is the relative topology for Y. Prove $\mathcal{F}_1 = \mathcal{F}_2$.

5. Let A and B be subsets of a space, each of which is closed in $A \cup B$. If $A \cup B$ and $A \cap B$ are connected, then A is connected (and so is B).

6. Let $C \subset B \subset A \subset X$, where $(X, \mathcal{T})$ is a space. Prove: If C is closed in B and B is closed in A, then C is closed in A.

7. Let A and B be subsets of a space, each of which is closed in $A \cup B$. Prove: If $A \cup B$ is connected and $A \cap B$ contains at most two points, then A is connected or B is connected.

Proof of 5. The conclusion is immediate if $A \subset B$ or $B \subset A$. So suppose $A \sim B$ and $B \sim A$ are non-void. Since A is closed in $A \cup B$, we have $B \sim A$ is open in $A \cup B$ (for $B \sim A$ is the complement of A in the subspace $A \cup B$). By 4(a), $B \sim A$ is open in $(B \sim A) \cup (A \sim B)$. Similarly $A \sim B$ is open in $(B \sim A) \cup (A \sim B)$. Therefore [by 4.8(b)] $B \sim A$ and $A \sim B$ are separated. Now

$$A \cup B \sim A \cap B = (B \sim A) \cup (A \sim B);$$

and by 3, $(A \sim B) \cup (A \cap B)$ is connected. But $(A \sim B) \cup (A \cap B) = A$, and A is connected. Similarly B is connected.

Proof of 7. (See 1.3 in Ch 1 for meaning of N_4.)

Suppose $\begin{cases} A = P_1 \cup P_2, & \text{where } P_1 \text{ and } P_2 \text{ are separated}; \\ B = P_3 \cup P_4, & \text{where } P_3 \text{ and } P_4 \text{ are separated}. \end{cases}$

(P_1 closed in A, A closed in $A \cup B$ and 6 imply P_1 closed in $A \cup B$. Similarly P_2, P_3 and P_4 are closed in $A \cup B$; and so is the union of any of these sets.)

Case I. $(A \cap B) \cap P_j = \emptyset$ for some j in N_4. Then

$$P_j \quad \text{and} \quad S = \bigcup \{P_i : \ i \in (N_4 \sim \{j\})\}$$

are disjoint and each is closed in $A \cup B$ while $P_j \cup S = A \cup B$.

Case II.   For each i in N_4, $(A \cap B) \cap P_i \neq \emptyset$. Then

$$A \cap B = \{p, q\}, \quad \text{where } p \neq q,$$

and the labeling may be chosen so that

$$P_1 \cap P_3 = \{p\} \quad \text{and} \quad P_2 \cap P_4 = \{q\}.$$

Then $P_1 \cup P_3$ and $P_2 \cup P_4$ are disjoint and each is closed in

$$A \cup B = (P_1 \cup P_3) \cup (P_2 \cup P_4).$$

Thus, in either case, $A \cup B$ is not connected if both A and B are not connected. Hence A is connected or B is connected.

Before concluding this section, let us return to 4.8 and note that the condition of A and B being separated depends solely on the topology for the subspace $A \cup B$. Hence a subset Y of a space X is a connected subset of X iff the subspace Y of X is a connected space. We can now prove:

Remark 5.9.   Let $A \subset Y \subset X$, where X is a topological space. Then the following statements are equivalent:

(a) A is a connected subset of the subspace Y.

(b) A is a connected subset of X.

Proof

(a) is equivalent to: The subspace A of Y is a connected space.

(b) is equivalent to: The subspace A of X is a connected space. But [by 4(b) in 5.8] the subspace A of Y is the same as the subspace A of X. Hence (a) is equivalent to (b).

6. Connected Subsets of R

Let $A \subset R$ and let $c \in R$. Then c is called a *lower bound for A* iff for each x in A, $c \leq x$; c is called a *greatest lower bound* (or *infimum*) *for A* iff c is a lower bound for A, and if y is a lower bound for A then $y \leq c$.   *Upper* *bound for A* and *least upper bound* (or *supremum*) *for A* are defined analogously. It is easy to show that there is at most one infimum for A; similarly for supremum. If the supremum for A exists, it is denoted by sup A; the infimum for A is denoted by inf A, if it exists.

When the student, at some time in his mathematical career, develops the system of real numbers, he finds that R is constructed by mortals (mathematicians) so that the following property holds.

Property 6.1. Each non-void subset of R with an upper bound has a least upper bound, and each non-void subset of R with a lower bound has a greatest lower bound.

Remark 6.2. If K is a connected subset of R, then:

(1)   If $a, b \in K$ with $a < b$, then K contains the closed interval from a to b.

Proof. Suppose $a, b \in K$ with $a < b$ and there is a number c in the closed interval from a to b such that $c \notin K$. Let

$$A = \{x: \ x \in K \ \text{ and } \ x < c\} \ \text{ and } \ B = \{x: \ x \in K \ \text{ and } \ c < x\}.$$

We see that

$$a \in A, \quad b \in B, \quad A \cap B = \varnothing \quad \text{and} \quad K = A \cup B.$$

Now A is the intersection of K and an open subset of R. (Specify such an open set.) Hence A is open in K. Also, B is open in K. Thus, by 4.8(b), A and B are separated. Hence K is not connected and 6.2 is proved.

We now prove the converse of 6.2.

Theorem 6.3. If K is a subset of R which satisfies condition (1) in 6.2, then K is connected.

Proof. Suppose $K = A \cup B$, where A and B are non-void disjoint sets labeled so that there are points a in A and b in B with $a < b$. Let $C = \{x: x \in A \text{ and } x < b\}$. Since $a \in C, C \neq \varnothing$. Also, C has an upper bound, namely b. In view of 6.1, let c be the least upper bound for C. Clearly $a \leq c \leq b$. By our hypothesis (1), $c \in K$; and since $K = A \cup B$,

$$c \in A \quad \text{or} \quad c \in B.$$

Case I. Suppose $c \in A$. The reader may show that in this case $c \in B^-$, and so

$$A \cap B^- \neq \varnothing.$$

Case II.   Suppose $c \in B$.   In this case $c \in A^-$ and $A^- \cap B \neq \varnothing$.

Thus in either case, A and B are not separated.   Since A and B are arbitrary non-void disjoint sets whose union is K, it follows that K cannot be written as the union of two separated sets.   Hence K is connected.

Combining 6.2 and 6.3, we obtain the following important theorem.

Theorem 6.4.   A subset K of R is connected iff K satisfies condition (1) in 6.2.

Let a, $b \in R$ with $a < b$.   Then each of the following sets is called an interval:

the open interval from a to b,
the closed interval from a to b,
the set $\{x: \ a \leq x < b\}$, and $\{x: \ a < x \leq b\}$.

Each of the following sets is called a ray:

$$\{x: \ x < a\}, \qquad \{x: \ x \leq a\}, \qquad \{x: \ a < x\} \quad \text{and} \quad \{x: \ a \leq x\}.$$

It is interesting to observe that 6.4 gives the following result.

Remark 6.5.   A subset K of R is connected iff K has one of the following forms:

(a) $K = \varnothing$.

(b) K consists of a single point.

(c) K is an interval.

(d) K is a ray.

(e) $K = R$.

Exercises 6.6

1.   What subsets of R are both open and closed?

2.   (a) Prove: If Y is a connected subset of R, then the subspace Y is locally connected.   (See 5.9.)

   (b) Give an example of a subspace of R which is not locally connected.

   (c) Give an example of a locally connected subspace of R which is not connected.

3. Let X be the set of all real numbers, and let $\mathcal{F}$ be the family generated by the family of all "half-open" intervals of the form $\{x: \quad a \leq x < b\}$, where $a, b \in R$ with $a < b$.   Prove:

(a) $\mathcal{F}$ is a topology for X.   (Use 3.5.)

(b) $(X, \mathcal{F})$ is a Hausdorff space.

(c) Each set of the form $\{x: \quad a \leq x < b\}$ is both open and closed (relative to the $\mathcal{F}$ topology).

(d) The space is not connected.

(e) The space is separable.

(f) There is no countable base for $\mathcal{F}$.

(g) $\{x: \quad a < x < b\}$ is $\mathcal{F}$-open but not $\mathcal{F}$-closed (where $a, b \in X$ and $a < b$).   What about the set $\{x: \quad a \leq x \leq b\}$?

7. Metric Spaces

Definition 7.1.   Let X be a set, and let d be a mapping of the set $X \times X$ into the set of non-negative real numbers.   The mapping d is called a *metric for X* iff for each triple x, y, z in X,

(a) $d(x, y) = 0$ iff $x = y$

and

(b) $d(x, y) + d(y, z) \geq d(z, x)$ (triangle inequality)

[where $d(x, y)$ denotes the image $d((x, y))$ of (x, y) under d].   The pair (X, d) is called a *metric space*, and the number $d(x, y)$ is called the *distance* between x and y.

It should be shown that $d(a, b) = d(b, a)$ for each pair a, b in X.   [Use (b) and (a) to show $d(a, b) \geq d(b, a)$ and $d(b, a) \geq d(a, b)$.]
Let p belong to the set X in 7.1, and let r be a *positive* real number.   The set

$$\{x: \quad x \in X \quad \text{and} \quad d(p, x) < r\}$$

is called an *r-sphere* (or *ball*) about p and is denoted by $S_r(p)$.

Remark 7.2.   Let (X, d) be a metric space, and let $\mathcal{B}$ be the family of all *r*-spheres in X (for all p in X and all positive real numbers r).   Then $\mathcal{B}$ is a base for a topology for X.

Proof. For each p in X and each positive number r, $d(p, p) = 0$, so $p \in S_r(p)$. Hence (a) in 3.5 holds.

Now suppose $S_r(p)$, $S_s(q) \in \mathcal{B}$ and $x \in S_r(p) \cap S_s(q)$. Let t be the minimum of $r - d(p, x)$ and $s - d(q, x)$. (Why is t positive?) To show

$$S_t(x) \subset S_r(p) \cap S_s(q),$$

let $y \in S_t(x)$. Then

$$d(p, y) \leq d(p, x) + d(x, y) < d(p, x) + t \leq d(p, x) + r - d(p, x) = r.$$

Therefore $y \in S_r(p)$. Similarly $y \in S_s(q)$, and we conclude that (b) in 3.5 holds. Hence $\mathcal{B}$ generates a topology for X.

Definition 7.3.   Let (X, d) be a metric space. The topology generated by the family $\mathcal{B}$ in 7.2 is called the *metric topology for X induced by d.*

In the future when a metric space is mentioned, it will be understood that the space is a topological space with the metric topology.

Examples 7.4.   (a) Let X be any set, and let d be defined so that for each pair x, y in X, $d(x, y) = 0$ if $x = y$, while $d(x, y) = 1$ if $x \neq y$. It is easy to show that d is a metric.

(b) For each pair x, y in R, let $d(x, y) = |x - y|$. In proving the triangle inequality for this d, one may use the inequality $|a + b| \leq |a| + |b|$ for each a, b in R. This metric is called the *usual metric* or *standard metric* for R. It is of interest to note that the topology induced by this metric is precisely the usual topology for R as defined in 1.3(c).

(c) For each pair p, q in E_2, where $p = (x, y)$ and $q = (a, b)$ let

$$d(p, q) = [(x - a)^2 + (y - b)^2]^{1/2}.$$

This metric is called the *standard* or *usual metric* for E_2. We see that the usual metric topology for E_2 is identical with the usual topology for E_2 given in 1.16. It will be shown in 7.9 that d is a metric.

Exercises 7.5

1. Let $p \in X$ where (X, d) is the metric space in 7.4(a). What is the set $S_r(p)$ in case

(a) $r > 1$?

(b) $0 < r \leq 1$?

(c) What is the metric topology for the space in 7.4(a)?

2. Prove that each metric space (with the metric topology) is a T_2 space.

3. For $p = (x, y)$ and $q = (a, b)$ in E_2, let $e(p, q) = |x - a| + |y - b|$.

   (a) Show that e is a metric for the set E_2.

   (b) Describe the spheres in this space.

   (c) Is the topology induced by e the usual topology for E_2? (Use 3.3.)

4. Let d be the standard metric for E_2, let $o = (0, 0)$, and for $p = (x, y)$ and $q = (a, b)$ in E_2, let

   $$e(p, q) = \begin{cases} d(p, o) + d(o, q) & \text{if } p, q \text{ and } o \text{ are not collinear,} \\ d(p, q) & \text{if } p, q \text{ and } o \text{ are collinear.} \end{cases}$$

   (a) Show that e is a metric for the set E_2.

   (b) Describe the spheres in this space.

   (c) Show that e does not induce the usual topology for E_2.

5. Let (X, d) be a metric space (with the metric topology), and let $p \in X$. Prove: The family of all r-spheres about p is a local base at p.

6. Prove: Each metric space is a first countable (topological) space. (Show that a countable subfamily of the family in 5 is a local base at p.)

Concerning 5, we might say that 5(a) in 3.9 tells us that the family of all r-spheres containing p is a local base at p, but 5 states more. It states the family of all r-spheres about p (i.e., with p as "center") is a local base at p.

Proof of 5. (Of course each r-sphere about p is a neighborhood of p.) Let U be any neighborhood of p. Then there is an r-sphere $S_r(q)$ such that $p \in S_r(q) \subset U$ (since the family of all spheres is a base for the topology). Now $d(p, q) < r$, and so $0 < r - d(p, q)$. Let $t = r - d(p, q)$. To show $S_t(p) \subset S_r(q)$, let $y \in S_t(p)$. Then

$$d(q, y) \leq d(q, p) + d(p, y) < d(q, p) + t = d(q, p) + r - d(q, p) = r.$$

Therefore

$$y \in S_r(q), \quad S_t(p) \subset S_r(q) \subset U,$$

and 5 is proved.

Definition 7.6.   Let p be a point in a metric space. By an ϵ-*neighborhood of* p we mean the ϵ-sphere $S_\epsilon(p)$ about p, where ϵ is a positive real number.

Exercise 5 and 2.7 give:

Remark 7.7.   Let (X, d) be a metric space, $A \subset X$, and $p \in X$.

(a) $p \in A'$ iff each ϵ-neighborhood of p contains a point of $A \sim \{p\}$ (i.e., for each $\epsilon > 0$ there is a q in A such that $0 < d(p, q) < \epsilon$).

(b) $p \in A^-$ iff each ϵ-neighborhood of p contains a point of A.

(c) A sequence S in X converges to p iff S is eventually in each ϵ-neighborhood of p.

By an n-*tuple of real numbers* (where $n \in N$), we mean a mapping x of N_n into R. As in the case of a sequence, we usually denote the image of i under x by x_i [rather than by $x(i)$]; and we may use $(x_1, x_2, \ldots, x_n)$ to denote the mapping x. We shall use E_n to denote the set of all n-tuples of real numbers where n is a fixed member of N.

Inequality 7.8.   If $a, b \in E_n$, then

$$\left| \sum_1^n a_i b_i \right| \leq \left[\sum_1^n a_i^2 \cdot \sum_1^n b_i^2 \right]^{1/2}.$$

Proof. For an arbitrary real number x,

$$0 \leq \sum_1^n (a_i x + b_i)^2 = x^2 \sum_1^n a_i^2 + 2x \sum_1^n a_i b_i + \sum_1^n b_i^2.$$

So the discriminant of the quadratic expression on the right must be ≤ 0; i.e.,

$$4 \left[\sum_1^n a_i b_i \right]^2 - 4 \sum_1^n a_i^2 \sum_1^n b_i^2 \leq 0$$

or

$$\left| \sum_1^n a_i b_i \right| \leq \left[\sum_1^n a_i^2 \sum_1^n b_i^2 \right]^{1/2}.$$

Example 7.9.   For each pair

$$x = (x_1, x_2, \ldots, x_n), \qquad y = (y_1, y_2, \ldots, y_n)$$

in E_n, let

$$d(x, y) = \left[\sum_1^n (x_i - y_i)^2 \right]^{1/2}.$$

The pair (E_n, d) is called the *Euclidean n-space* or the *n-dimensional Euclidean space*.

Clearly (a) in 7.1 is satisfied by the d in 7.9.   To prove (b) holds for this d, let $x, y, z \in E_n$; and let $a_i = x_i - y_i$ and $b_i = y_i - z_i$ so that $a_i + b_i = x_i - z_i$ for each i in N_n.   Now from 7.8,

$$(1) \qquad \left[\sum_1^n a_i^2 \sum_1^n b_i^2 \right]^{1/2} \geq \sum_1^n a_i b_i.$$

Multiplying each side of (1) by 2 and then adding

$$\sum_1^n a_i^2 + \sum_1^n b_i^2$$

to each side, we have

$$\left[\left(\sum_1^n a_i^2 \right)^{1/2} + \left(\sum_1^n b_i^2 \right)^{1/2} \right]^2 \geq \sum_1^n (a_i + b_i)^2,$$

and so

$$\left(\sum_1^n a_i^2 \right)^{1/2} + \left(\sum_1^n b_i^2 \right)^{1/2} \geq \left[\sum_1^n (a_i + b_i)^2 \right]^{1/2},$$

i.e.,

$$d(x, y) + d(y, z) \geq d(x, z).$$

For our next example we would like to show that if x and y are sequences of real numbers (i.e., x and y are mappings of N into R) such that each of the series

$$(2) \qquad \sum_1^\infty x_i^2 \quad \text{and} \quad \sum_1^\infty y_i^2$$

converges, then the series

$$\sum_1^\infty (x_i - y_i)^2$$

converges.

Suppose each series in (2) converges.   For each i in N,

$$(|x_i| - |y_i|)^2 \geq 0,$$

so that

$$(3) \qquad x_i^2 + y_i^2 \geq |2 x_i y_i|.$$

Since each series in (2) converges,

$$\sum_1^\infty (x_i^2 + y_i^2)$$

must converge; and hence from (3),

$$\sum_1^\infty |2 x_i y_i|$$

converges.   Therefore

$$\sum_1^\infty 2 x_i y_i$$

converges and so does

$$\sum_{1}^{\infty} (x_i^2 - 2x_i y_i + y_i^2),$$

i.e.,

$$\sum_{1}^{\infty} (x_i - y_i)^2$$

converges.

Example 7.10.   Let H be the set of all sequences x in R such that $\sum_{1}^{\infty} x_i^2$ converges; and for each x, y in H, let

$$d(x, y) = \left[\sum_{1}^{\infty} (x_i - y_i)^2 \right]^{1/2}.$$

(From the preceding paragraph, we know the series in the brackets converges.) The pair (H, d) is called the *real Hilbert space*.

It is clear that d satisfies (a) in 7.1.   To verify (b), let $x, y, z \in H$.   Then for any one n in N,

$$\left[\sum_{1}^{n} (x_i - y_i)^2 \right]^{1/2} + \left[\sum_{1}^{n} (y_i - z_i)^2 \right]^{1/2} \geq \left[\sum_{1}^{n} (x_i - z_i)^2 \right]^{1/2},$$

because (as we have shown) the triangle inequality holds in E_n.   Now "taking the limit of each side as n becomes large" we see that

$$d(x, y) + d(y, z) \geq d(x, z).$$

Therefore d is a metric for H.

Exercises 7.11

1. If in 7.1 condition (a) is replaced by the condition $d(x, y) = 0$ if $x = y$, then [keeping (b)] d is called a *pseudo-metric for X*, and (X, d) is called a *pseudo-metric space*.   We did not use the other half of (a) in the proof of 7.2.   So we realize we may induce a pseudo-metric topology for X in the manner used to introduce a metric topology.   According to 2 in 7.5, each metric space is a T_2 space. Give an example of a pseudo-metric space which (with the pseudo-metric topology) is not a T_1 space.

2. If in 7.1 we drop the triangle inequality and add the condition $d(x, y) = d(y, x)$ for each x, y in X, then, keeping (a) as it is in 7.1, (X, d) is called a *semi-metric space*.   Give an example of a semi-metric space in which the family of all r-spheres does not generate a topology (r-spheres being defined just as in metric spaces).

A solution for 2. (Give your own example first.)   Let $X = R \cup \{b\}$, where b denotes something other than a number, say the letter b.   Define d as follows:

$$d(x, y) = |x - y| \quad \text{if } x, y \in R,$$
$$d(b, x) = d(x, b) = 7 \text{ if } x \in R \quad \text{and } x \neq 2,$$
$$d(b, 2) = d(2, b) = 3,$$
$$d(b, b) = 0.$$

Now $2 \in S_6(b) \cap S_2(2)$, but there is no r-sphere contained in this set which contains the element 2.   Hence, by 3.5, the family of r-spheres does not generate a topology for X.

8. Other Approaches to a Topological Space

Theorem 8.1.   Let $\mathcal{C}$ be a collection of subsets of a set X, and let $\mathcal{T}$ be the family of all complements of members of $\mathcal{C}$.   Then $\mathcal{T}$ is a topology for X iff (where X is the underlying set)

(a) the intersection of each subfamily of $\mathcal{C}$ belongs to $\mathcal{C}$,

(b) the union of each finite subfamily of $\mathcal{C}$ belongs to $\mathcal{C}$.

Moreover, the family of all $\mathcal{T}$-closed sets is precisely the family $\mathcal{C}$.

The simple proof of this theorem (which makes use of the DeMorgan theorem) is left to the reader.

In our approach to a topological space (Def 1.1 and 1.2) we essentially used the concept "open set" as the primitive notion (without mentioning the words "open set" immediately).   Conditions (a) and (b) in 1.1 were taken as the axioms for our system.   "Closed set" (as well as all other concepts in an arbitrary topological space) was defined in terms of the basic notion "open set".

Theorem 8.1 suggests that we might have begun with "closed set" as our primitive notion and used (a) and (b) in 8.1 as our axioms.   Then we would have defined an open set as the complement of a closed set;   and the study of the pair $(X, \mathcal{C})$, where $\mathcal{C}$ is the family of all closed sets, would be logically equivalent to the study of a topological space as defined in 1.2.

There are other possibilities.   Consider the following theorem.

Theorem 8.2.   Let X be a set, and let f be a function which associates with each subset A of X a subset $f(A)$ of X such that

(1) $f(\varnothing) = \varnothing$,

(2) for each A, $A \subset f(A)$,

(3) for each A, $f(f(A)) = f(A)$, and

(4) for each A and B, $f(A \cup B) = f(A) \cup f(B)$.

Let $\mathcal{C}$ be the family of all subsets A of X such that $f(A) = A$. Then the family $\mathcal{T}$ of all complements of members of $\mathcal{C}$ is a topology for X, and $f(A)$ is the $\mathcal{T}$-closure of A for each subset A of X.

Proof. To show that $\mathcal{C}$ satisfies (a) in 8.1, first note that if $A \subset B \subset X$, then $f(A) \subset f(B)$; for

$$f(B) = f((B \sim A) \cup A) = f(B \sim A) \cup f(A) \supset f(A)$$

because of (4). Now let $\mathcal{A}$ be any subfamily of $\mathcal{C}$, and let $B = \bigcap \mathcal{A}$. Then for each A in $\mathcal{A}$, $B \subset A$ and so

$$f(B) \subset f(A) = A.$$

Hence

$$f(B) \subset \bigcap \mathcal{A} = B.$$

But $B \subset f(B)$ by (2). Therefore

$$B = f(B) \quad \text{and} \quad B \in \mathcal{C}.$$

So (a) in 8.1 is satisfied.

Now suppose $A, B \in \mathcal{C}$. Then

$$f(A \cup B) = f(A) \cup f(B) = A \cup B,$$

and so $A \cup B \in \mathcal{C}$. By induction, the union of each non-void finite subfamily of $\mathcal{C}$ is a member of $\mathcal{C}$. By (1), $\varnothing \in \mathcal{C}$, and so the union of each finite subfamily of $\mathcal{C}$ is a member of $\mathcal{C}$. Thus (a) and (b) in 8.1 are satisfied by $\mathcal{C}$; and by 8.1, $\mathcal{T}$ is a topology for X.

Now let $A \subset X$. We want to show that $f(A) = A^-$. By 8.1, $\mathcal{C}$ is the family of all $\mathcal{T}$-closed sets. Thus

$$A^- \in \mathcal{C} \quad \text{and} \quad f(A^-) = A^-;$$

and since $A \subset A^-$, we have

(5) $$f(A) \subset f(A^-) = A^-.$$

By (3), $f(A) \in \mathcal{C}$, and so $f(A)$ is a closed set which by (2) contains A. Therefore

(6) $$A^- \subset f(A).$$

Thus (5) and (6) give $f(A) = A^-$ and 8.2 is proved.

Definition 8.3.   Let X be a set and let $\mathcal{P}$ be the family of all subsets of X. A mapping f of $\mathcal{P}$ into $\mathcal{P}$ is called a *closure function* for X iff f satisfies conditions (1)–(4) in 8.2, and conditions (1)–(4) are called the *Kuratowski closure axioms*.

In view of 8.2, a closure function f for a set X induces a topology for X such that the closure of each subset A of X is the set $f(A)$. In view of 1.15, a topology for X induces a closure function for X. Thus whether one uses our axioms in 1.1 for the primitive notion "open set" or axioms (1)–(4) for the primitive notion "closure", the mathematical systems are essentially logically equivalent. So the reader will understand the situation if he finds in some book that a topological space is defined to be a set X together with a closure function for X (or to be a set X together with a family of subsets of X satisfying the conditions of 8.1).

We give one further approach to a topological space. Some authors define a topological space as a set X in which there is associated with each point p in X a non-void family of subsets of X, called neighborhoods of p, in such a way that the following four axioms are satisfied:

(a) For each p in X, each neighborhood of p contains p.

(b) If U is a neighborhood of p and $q \in U$, then there is a neighborhood V of q such that $V \subset U$.

(c) If U and V are neighborhoods of p, then there is a neighborhood W of p such that $W \subset U \cap V$.

(d) If $p, q \in X$ with $p \neq q$, then there is a neighborhood U of p such that $q \notin U$.

In such a system one defines "open set" in an appropriate way. (What is this appropriate way?) Then he has an example of what we have called a topological space. But beginning with our definition of a topological space and our definition of "neighborhood of a point", condition (d) need not be satisfied. For example, in an indiscrete space with more than one point, (d) is not satisfied. So this last definition of a topological space is in no sense equivalent to our definition in 1.2. Each system satisfying (a)–(d) is a T_1 space.

We have seen that each metric for a set X induces a topology for X. We have also seen that, given a topology $\mathcal{T}$ for X, there may exist a metric for X whose induced metric topology is precisely the original topology $\mathcal{T}$. For example, given the discrete space, there is a metric (the one given in 7.4(a)) such that the metric topology is the discrete topology. Also the usual topology for R is induced by the usual metric for R. We then ask the question: Given any topological space $(X, \mathcal{T})$, is there always a metric for X which induces the topology $\mathcal{T}$? What do you say before reading the answer?

To answer the question, we recall that each metric topology is a T_2 topology. But there are topological spaces which are not T_2 spaces. Thus if we take a space which is not a T_2 space, there is no metric which induces the given topology. Hence the notion of a topological space is a more general concept than that of a metric space.

A topological space $(X, \mathscr{T})$ is said to be metrizable iff there is a metric for X which induces the topology $\mathscr{T}$. The next natural question is: What conditions on a topological space are necessary and sufficient in order that the space be metrizable? This is a rather complex problem, and its treatment is postponed.

Miscellaneous Exercises 8.4

1. Let $\mathcal{C}$ be a collection of subsets of a topological space. Prove:

   (a) If $B, D \in \mathcal{C}$ and $D \subset B$, then $D^- \subset B^-$.

   (b) $(\bigcap \mathcal{C})^- \subset \bigcap \{A^- : A \in \mathcal{C}\}$; $(\bigcup \mathcal{C})^- \supset \bigcup \{A^- : A \in \mathcal{C}\}$.

   (c) If $B, D \in \mathcal{C}$, then $B^- \sim D^- \subset (B \sim D)^-$.

2. Let G be an open subset of a space X and let $H \subset X$. Prove:

   (a) $H^- \cap G \subset (H \cap G)^-$.

   (b) If H is dense in X, then $G \subset (H \cap G)^-$.

3. Let $\mathscr{F}$ be the family consisting of $\varnothing$, R, and all open right rays in R. (A subset G of R is called an open right ray iff $G = \{x : x > a\}$ for some a in R.)

   (a) Prove $\mathscr{F}$ is a topology for R.

   (b) Specify the $\mathscr{F}$-closed subsets of R.

   (c) Is the space $(R, \mathscr{F})$ connected?

   (d) Prove this space is not T_1 (and hence not T_2).

   (e) If $p \in R$, what is the derived set of $\{p\}$?

4. Prove: If F is a finite subset of a T_1 space, then $F' = \varnothing$. (See 9 in 1.18.)

5. Specify a Lindelöf space in 1.3 which is not second countable. Can you give a Lindelöf space of your own which is not second countable?

6. See 1 in 3.9 and prove: If Y is a closed subset of a Lindelöf space, then the subspace Y is a Lindelöf space.

7. (a) Prove: If $\mathscr{T}_1$ and $\mathscr{T}_2$ are topologies for a set X, then $\mathscr{T}_1 \cap \mathscr{T}_2$ is a topology for X but $\mathscr{T}_1 \cup \mathscr{T}_2$ may fail to be a topology for X.

(b) **Prove:** The intersection of any collection of topologies for a set X is a topology for X.

(c) **Prove:** For each collection of topologies for a set X, there is a smallest topology for X which is larger than each of the given topologies. ("$\mathscr{T}$ is smaller than $\mathscr{F}$" means $\mathscr{T} \subset \mathscr{F}$.) (See the first paragraph following 3.10.)

8.   A binary relation B on a set X is called an *anti-reflexive simple order relation* on X iff

(a) $x, y \in X$ and $x \neq y$ implies xBy or yBx,

(b) xBy implies $x \neq y$, and

(c) B is transitive.

When B is such a relation on X, it is customary to use "$x < y$" to denote "xBy" and to say in this case that x *precedes* y or x *is less than* y. We also write "$y > x$" to mean "$x < y$" and say that y *follows* x or y *is greater than* x. For each a in X, the set $\{x : x < a\}$ is called the *open left ray from* a, and $\{x : a < x\}$ is called the *open right ray from* a.

　　Prove that not both xBy and yBx can hold (where B is an anti-reflexive simple order relation).

9.   Let B be an anti-reflexive simple order relation on a set X, and let S be the family of all open rays in X. (See 8.) The topology which has S for a subbase is called the *order* (or *B-order*) *topology for* X. We write $x \leq y$ iff $x = y$ or $x < y$. State what we would naturally mean by an *upper bound* and by a *least upper bound* (or *supremum*) for a subset A of X. X is said to be *order complete* iff each non-void subset of X with an upper bound has a least upper bound; and X is said *to have no gaps* iff for $x, y \in X$ with $x < y$, there is some z in X such that $x < z < y$.

(a) Prove that X with the order topology is connected iff X is order complete and has no gaps. (*Hint:* See the proofs of 6.2 and 6.3.)

(b) (If $Y \subset X$, then Y inherits the $<$ simple order relation from X.) (If $<$ is the usual less than relation on R, then the order topology for R is identical with the usual topology for R, i.e., the family of all open rays in R is a subbase for the usual topology for R—as observed earlier.) Give an example of a subset Y or R such that the usual $<$ order topology for Y is not the same as the relative topology for Y.

10. Let $\mathcal{B}$ be a base for a topology $\mathcal{T}$ for a set X. Prove: If each cover for X with members of $\mathcal{B}$ has a countable subcover for X, then $(X, \mathcal{T})$ is a Lindelöf space.

11. Let $\mathcal{B}$ and X be the same as in 3 of 6.6.
    (a) Prove: If $\mathcal{A} \subset \mathcal{B}$, then there is a countable subfamily $\mathcal{C}$ of $\mathcal{A}$ such that $\bigcup \mathcal{C} = \bigcup \mathcal{A}$. (It is convenient to use $[a, b)$ to denote $\{x: a \leq x < b\}$ and to use $(a, b]$, (a, b) and $[a, b]$ to denote the other respective types of intervals.) [*Hint:* (1) Let $\mathcal{D}$ be the family of all open intervals (a, b) where $[a, b) \in \mathcal{A}$, and use 3.8 (applied to the usual topology for R which is second countable) to conclude there is a countable subfamily of $\mathcal{D}$ whose union is equal to $\bigcup \mathcal{D}$. (2) Then observe that all but a countable number of points in $\bigcup \mathcal{A}$ are in $\bigcup \mathcal{D}$; this is so because a family of disjoint intervals in R is countable since there is a one-to-one mapping of such a family into the rationals—pick one rational number from each interval.]

    (b) Prove that the space in 3 of 6.6 is a Lindelöf space.

12. (a) Prove: If $\mathcal{A}$ is a collection of closed intervals in R, then there is a countable subfamily $\mathcal{C}$ of $\mathcal{A}$ such that $\bigcup \mathcal{C} = \bigcup \mathcal{A}$. (In our language, an interval in R always contains more than one point. When we call $[a, b]$ an interval, it is understood that $a < b$.)

    (b) Prove: If $\mathcal{A}$ is a collection of intervals in R, then there is a countable subfamily $\mathcal{C}$ of $\mathcal{A}$ such that $\bigcup \mathcal{C} = \bigcup \mathcal{A}$. [*Hint:* Break up $\mathcal{A}$ into the four subfamilies consisting respectively of the closed intervals in $\mathcal{A}$, the open members of $\mathcal{A}$, the members of $\mathcal{A}$ of the form $[a, b)$, and those of the form $(a, b]$.]

13. Let X be a set with the finite complement topology, and let S be a sequence in X. (Let us say that S repeats the point p infinitely many times iff $\{n: S_n = p\}$ is an infinite set.) Prove: In this space, S converges to a point q of X iff no point in $X \sim \{q\}$ is repeated infinitely many times. (Note this is an answer to 1 in 2.8.)

3

Mappings of Topological Spaces

I. Continuous Functions

We now consider an all-important concept from analysis—the concept of a continuous function.

Definition I.I.   Let $(X, \mathcal{T})$ and $(Y, \mathcal{F})$ be topological spaces, and let f be a mapping of X into Y.

(a) Let $p \in X$. The mapping f is said to be *continuous at p* iff for each neighborhood U of $f(p)$, there is a neighborhood V of p such that $f[V] \subset U$.

(b) The mapping f is said to be *continuous* iff it is continuous at each point of X.

The proof of our first theorem is left especially for you.

Theorem I.2.   Let f be a mapping of a space X into a space Y, let $p \in X$, $\mathcal{U}$ a local base at $f(p)$, and $\mathcal{V}$ a local base at p. The function f is continuous at p iff for each U in $\mathcal{U}$ there is a V in $\mathcal{V}$ such that $f[V] \subset U$.

Exercise 5 in 7.5 of Ch 2 gives the following:

Corollary I.3.   Let f be a mapping of X into Y, where (X, d) and (Y, e) are metric spaces, and let $p \in X$. Then f is continuous at p iff for each ϵ-sphere U about $f(p)$, there is a δ-sphere V about p such that $f[V] \subset U$, i.e., iff for each real number $\epsilon > 0$, there is a number $\delta > 0$ such that $d(p, q) < \delta$ implies $e(f(p), f(q)) < \epsilon$.

We leave it to the reader to rephrase this theorem in a familiar form (using absolute values of differences) for the case in which both spaces are R (with the standard metric).

The next theorem gives several conditions, each of which is equivalent to continuity of a function (—not continuity at a point).

Theorem I.4.   Let f be a mapping of a space X into a space Y. The following statements are equivalent.

(a) The function f is continuous.

(b) For each x in X and each neighborhood U of $f(x)$, there is a neighborhood V of x such that $f[V] \subset U$.

(c) For each x in X and each member U of a local base at $f(x)$, there is a neighborhood V of x such that $f[V] \subset U$.

(d) For each open subset G of Y, $f^{-1}[G]$ is open in X.

(e) The inverse image of each closed subset of Y is closed in X.

(f) For each subset A of X, $f[A^-] \subset (f[A])^-$.

(g) For each subset B of Y, $(f^{-1}[B])^- \subset f^{-1}[B^-]$.

Proof. (a) $\longleftrightarrow$ (b):   Condition (b) is merely the condition for continuity of f at each point of X (see 1.1(a)), and in view of 1.1(b) this is equivalent to the continuity of f.

(a) $\longleftrightarrow$ (c):   The family of *all* neighborhoods of a point x is a local base at x. So, in view of 1.2, condition (c) is equivalent to the continuity of f at each point of X;   and, by 1.1(b), this is equivalent to continuity of f.

(b) $\longleftrightarrow$ (d):   Suppose (b) holds, let G be an open subset of Y, and suppose $x \in f^{-1}[G]$. Then $f(x) \in G$, and G is a neighborhood of $f(x)$. By hypothesis (b), there is a neighborhood V of x such that $f[V] \subset G$, i.e., $V \subset f^{-1}[G]$. Therefore $f^{-1}[G]$ is open (Ch 2, 1.5, 5). So (b) implies (d). Now suppose (d) holds, $x \in X$ and U is any neighborhood of $f(x)$. Then U is open, and by hypothesis $f^{-1}[U]$ is open. Also $x \in f^{-1}[U]$ and so $f^{-1}[U]$ is a neighborhood of x. Furthermore, $f[f^{-1}[U]] \subset U$, and (d) implies (b).

(d) $\longleftrightarrow$ (e): Suppose (d) holds, and let H be a closed subset of Y. Then $X \sim f^{-1}[H] = f^{-1}[Y \sim H]$, which is open by hypothesis (d). Therefore $f^{-1}[H]$ is closed, and (d) implies (e). The similar proof of the other half is left for you.

(b) $\longrightarrow$ (f): Let $A \subset X$ and suppose $y \in f[A^-]$. Then there is some x in A^- such that $f(x) = y$. Let U be any neighborhood of y. By hypothesis (b) there is a neighborhood V of x such that $f[V] \subset U$. Now (by 1.13 in Ch 2) V contains a point z in A, and so $f(z) \in f[A] \cap U$. Therefore (by 1.13 in Ch 2 again) $y \in (f[A])^-$, and (f) follows.

(f) $\longrightarrow$ (g): Suppose (f) holds and let $B \subset Y$. Let $A = f^{-1}[B]$. Then by hypothesis

$$f[A^-] \subset (f[A])^- \subset B^- \text{ (since } f[A] \subset B).$$

This means

$$(A)^- \subset f^{-1}[B^-],$$

i.e.,

$$(f^{-1}[B])^- \subset f^{-1}[B^-].$$

(g) $\longrightarrow$ (e): Let B be a closed subset of Y. By hypothesis (g),

$$(f^{-1}[B])^- \subset f^{-1}[B^-] = f^{-1}[B],$$

and therefore $f^{-1}[B]$ must be closed.

(It should be observed that, due to transitivity of "equivalent" and transitivity of "implies", any two of the conditions in 1.4 are now shown to be equivalent.)

We give one further simple condition equivalent to continuity of a function, which occasionally turns out to be very convenient.

Theorem 1.5.   Let f be a mapping of a space X into a space Y, and let $\mathcal{S}$ be a subbase for the topology for Y. Then f is continuous iff the inverse image of each member of $\mathcal{S}$ is open in X.

Proof. Since each member of $\mathcal{S}$ is open in Y, the "only if" part of 1.5 follows from 1.4 $((a) \longrightarrow (d))$. Now suppose $f^{-1}[U]$ is open for each U in $\mathcal{S}$, and let $\mathcal{B}$ be the family of all finite intersections of members of $\mathcal{S}$. Let $B \in \mathcal{B}$. Then (except for the trivial case where $B = Y$, in which case $f^{-1}[B] = X$)

$$B = U_1 \cap U_2 \cap \ldots \cap U_n$$

for some n in N where $U_i \in \mathcal{S}$. By hypothesis $f^{-1}[U_i]$ is open. Hence $f^{-1}[B]$ is open since (by 2 in 3.10 of Ch 1)

$$f^{-1}[B] = f^{-1}[U_i] \cap f^{-1}[U_2] \cap \ldots \cap f^{-1}[U_n].$$

Finally, let G be any open subset of Y. Then (since $\mathcal{B}$ is a base) $G = \bigcup \mathcal{C}$ where $\mathcal{C} \subset \mathcal{B}$. Again by 2 in 3.10 of Ch 1,

$$f^{-1}[G] = \bigcup \{f^{-1}[B]: \ B \in \mathcal{C}\}.$$

Therefore $f^{-1}[G]$ is open and f is continuous by 1.4 $((d) \longrightarrow (a))$.

In proving that a given function is continuous, you will often find that it is perhaps most convenient to prove the condition in 1.4(d) or the condition in 1.5.

Exercises I.6

1. Suppose the function f in 1.1 is a constant function, i.e., for each x in X, $f(x) = c$ for some fixed c in Y. Prove f is continuous.

2. Let $(X, \mathscr{T})$ be a topological space, and let f be the identity mapping of X onto X (for each x in X, $f(x) = x$). Prove f is continuous.

3. Let $X = R$, let $\mathscr{F}$ be the finite complement topology for X, and let $\mathscr{U}$ be the usual topology for R.

   (a) Let f be the identity mapping of $(X, \mathscr{F})$ onto $(R, \mathscr{U})$; i.e., f is the identity mapping of $X \ (= R)$ onto R and the topology for our domain set X is $\mathscr{F}$ while the topology of our range set R is $\mathscr{U}$. Is f continuous?

   (b) Let g be the identity mapping of $(R, \mathscr{U})$ onto $(X, \mathscr{F})$. Is g continuous?

4. Let $a \in R$ and let f be the mapping of R into R defined by $f(x) = ax$ for each x in R. Let g be the function on R to R defined by $g(x) = x^2$. Taking the family S of all open rays in R as a subbase for the usual topology for R, use 1.5 to prove that each of the mappings f and g is continuous. (Here the usual topology for R is understood in all cases, since no other topology is mentioned.)

5. Let g be a mapping of a space X into a space Y, and let f be a mapping of Y into a space Z. Prove:

   (a) For each subset A of Z,
   $$(f \circ g)^{-1}[A] = g^{-1}[f^{-1}[A]],$$
   where $f \circ g$ is the composition mapping defined in 4.8 of Ch 1.

   (b) If g and f are continuous, then $f \circ g$ is continuous.

6. Use 4 and 5(b) to prove the function $h: \ R \longrightarrow R$, defined by $h(x) = ax^2$, is continuous.

7. Let f be a mapping of a space X into a space Y. What may be said about the continuity of f in case:

   (a) X is a discrete space?

   (b) Y is indiscrete?

8.   Let f be a mapping of a *set* X into a *space* Y.

(a) Is it always possible to assign a topology for X so that f is continuous?

(b) What is the smallest topology for X which makes f continuous?

9.   For each a in a set A, let f_a be a mapping of a set Z into a space X_a. What is the smallest topology $\mathcal{T}$ for Z which makes all of the given functions f_a continuous?

Answer to 8.   (a) The discrete topology for X will make f continuous [1.4(a) and (d)] since for each open subset G of Y, $f^{-1}[G]$ is open relative to the discrete topology for X.

(b) Let $\mathcal{F}$ be the family of all subsets of the form $f^{-1}[U]$, where U is open in Y. [In view of 1.4(a) and (d)] if $\mathcal{T}$ is a topology for X, then f is continuous (relative to $\mathcal{T}$ and the given topology for Y) iff $\mathcal{F} \subset \mathcal{T}$. Thus we want the smallest topology which contains $\mathcal{F}$. But because of 2 in 3.10 of Ch 1, $\mathcal{F}$ is itself a topology for X. So $\mathcal{F}$ is the smallest topology which contains $\mathcal{F}$.

Answer to 9.   Let $\mathcal{S}$ be the family of *all* sets of the form $f_a^{-1}[U]$, where U is an open subset of X_a for a in A. Just as in 8(b), a topology $\mathcal{U}$ for Z will make all of the given functions continuous iff $\mathcal{S} \subset \mathcal{U}$. Hence, in view of the paragraph immediately following 3.10 in Ch 2, the smallest topology for Z, which makes all of the given functions continuous, is the topology $\mathcal{T}$ determined by $\mathcal{S}$ as a subbase.

Remark 1.7.   The topology $\mathcal{T}$ required in 9 of 1.6 is the topology determined by $\mathcal{S}$ as a subbase, where $\mathcal{S}$ is the family of all sets of the form $f_a^{-1}[U]$, where U is open in X_a and $a \in A$.

Of course a base for the topology $\mathcal{T}$ in 9 is the family $\mathcal{B}$ of all finite intersections of members of $\mathcal{S}$. A finite subfamily of $\mathcal{S}$ might include several sets of the form

$$f_a^{-1}[V_1], \quad f_a^{-1}[V_2], \quad \ldots, \quad f_a^{-1}[V_n]$$

for a fixed a in A (together with other sets $f_b^{-1}[V]$, where $b \in A$ and $b \neq a$), where the V's are open. But we note that for a fixed a,

$$f_a^{-1}[V_1] \cap f_a^{-1}[V_2] \cap \ldots \cap f_a^{-1}[V_n] = f_a^{-1}[V_1 \cap V_2 \cap \ldots \cap V_n] = f_a^{-1}[U],$$

where $U = V_1 \cap V_2 \cap \ldots \cap V_n$; and U is open in X_a if the V's are open in X_a. So if a given finite intersection of members of $\mathcal{S}$ includes sets $f_a^{-1}[V_1], \ldots, f_a^{-1}[V_n]$ for a fixed a, these sets can be associated together and written as $f_a^{-1}[U]$, a single member of $\mathcal{S}$.   Thus:

Remark I.8.   One base for the topology required in 9 of 1.6 is the family $\mathcal{B}$ defined as follows: A subset B of Z belongs to $\mathcal{B}$ iff $B = \cap \{f_a^{-1}[U_a]: \quad a \in F\}$ for some finite subset F of A and where U_a is an open subset of X_a for each a in F.

The last two remarks were recorded for future reference.

Let f be a mapping of a space X into a space Y.   Recall that a sequence in X is a mapping S of N into X.   Actually, we often denote the sequence S by listing the images under S of $1, 2, 3, \ldots$.   Thus $S_1, S_2, S_3, \ldots$ denotes the sequence S.   So $f(S_1), f(S_2), f(S_3), \ldots$ denotes the sequence in Y which maps i into $f(S_i)$ for each i in N.   Thus the latter sequence is merely the composition mapping $f \circ S$ as defined by 4.8 in Ch 1.   If f is continuous at a point p in X and S converges to p, then the sequence $f(S_1), f(S_2), f(S_3), \ldots$ converges to $f(p)$.   We would like to state this theorem formally and leave its proof for you.

Theorem I.9.   Let f be a mapping of a space X into a space Y, and let $p \in X$.   If f is continuous at p, then $f \circ S$ converges to $f(p)$ for each sequence S in X which converges to p.

The converse of 1.9 is not valid in general spaces, as is shown by 1.10(a) which follows.

Example I.10.   Let $X = R$, and let $\mathcal{C}$ be the "countable complement" topology for X, i.e., a subset G of X belongs to $\mathcal{C}$ iff $G = \varnothing$ or $X \sim G$ is countable.   Let $\mathcal{U}$ be the usual topology for R.

(a) Let $f\colon X \longrightarrow R$ be the identity mapping of the space $(X, \mathcal{C})$ into the space $(R, \mathcal{U})$.

(b) Let $g\colon R \longrightarrow X$ be the identity mapping of the space $(R, \mathcal{U})$ into the space $(X, \mathcal{C})$.

Notice: If S is a sequence in X which $\mathcal{C}$-converges to p, then $f \circ S$ $\mathcal{U}$-converges to $f(p)$. [Of course, $f(p) = p$ and $f \circ S = S$.] But f is not continuous. (Show this.)

We should also notice that g is not continuous at any point in R.   (Th 1.9 shows that g is not continuous at 0, for the sequence $1, 1/2, \ldots, 1/n, \ldots$ $\mathcal{U}$-converges to 0, but $g(1), g(1/2), \ldots, g(1/n), \ldots$ does not $\mathcal{C}$-converge to 0.)   (Show directly that g is not continuous by specifying a $\mathcal{C}$-open subset U of X such that $g^{-1}[U]$ is not $\mathcal{U}$-open in R.)

If we suppose that the domain space X in 1.9 is first countable, then the converse theorem is valid.

Theorem 1.11.   Let f be a mapping of a first countable space X into a space Y, and let $p \in X$. Then f is continuous at p iff $f \circ S$ converges to $f(p)$ for each sequence S in X which converges to p.

Proof. The "only if" part follows from 1.9. We prove the contrapositive of the "if" part. Suppose f is not continuous at p, and (2.5 in Ch 2) let $\{V_1, V_2, \ldots\}$ be a monotone decreasing countable local base at p. Then there is some neighborhood U of $f(p)$ for which there is no neighborhood V of p such that $f[V] \subset U$. Thus for each i in N, let S_i be a point in V_i such that $f(S_i) \notin U$.

Since $\{V_1, V_2, \ldots\}$ is a monotone decreasing local base at p, it follows that the sequence S, just obtained, converges to p. But $f \circ S$ does not converge to $f(p)$, since $f \circ S$ is not eventually in U (for each i in N, $f(S_i) \notin U$).

Exercise 1.12

Let $f: X \longrightarrow R$ and $g: X \longrightarrow R$ be continuous mappings of a space X into R, let $h: X \longrightarrow R$ be defined by $h(x) = f(x) + g(x)$ for each x in X, and let $k: X \longrightarrow R$ be defined by $k(x) = f(x)g(x)$ for each x in X. Prove: (a) h is continuous. (b) k is continuous. (To do this exercise, use 1.4(c), taking as a local base at $h(p)$ the family of ϵ-spheres about $h(p)$. To prove k is continuous at an arbitrary point p in X, you may use the equality

$$f(x)g(x) - f(p)g(p)$$
$$= [f(x) - f(p)][g(x) - g(p)] + f(p)[g(x) - g(p)] + g(p)[f(x) - f(p)].)$$

2. Restrictions and Extensions of Mappings

Frequently we encounter a function $f: A \longrightarrow R$ where A is a proper subset of R and f is not defined on $R \sim A$. When we refer to the continuity of f in this case, it is understood that A is treated as a subspace of R (unless some topology is specified for A). Thus f is continuous at a point p in A iff for each ϵ-sphere U about $f(p)$, there is a δ-sphere V about p such that $f[V \cap A] \subset U$, since $V \cap A$ is a base neighborhood of p in the subspace A.

In general, let $f: A \longrightarrow Y$ be a mapping where Y is a space and A is a subset of a space X. Then when we refer to the continuity of f, we are considering A as a subspace of X. As a matter of fact, when we use a subset A of a space X in any context which requires a topology for A, we understand that A is to have the relative topology of X.

On the other hand, we sometimes have a mapping f of a space X into a space Y but we are interested in f only at points in some subset A of X. The function $g\colon\ A \longrightarrow Y$ defined by

$$g(x) = f(x) \text{ for each } x \text{ in } A$$

is called the *restriction of f to A* and may be denoted by f_A. (Some writers use f/A to denote the restriction of f to A.)

Definition 2.1.   A mapping f of a space X into a space Y is said to be *continuous on A* (where $A \subset X$) iff f_A is continuous (using the relative topology for A).

Theorem 2.2.   Let A be a subset of a space X, and let f be a mapping of X into a space Y.

(a) If $f\colon\ X \longrightarrow Y$ is continuous at a point p of A, then $f_A\colon\ A \longrightarrow Y$ is continuous at p.

(b) If $f\colon\ X \longrightarrow Y$ is continuous at each point of A, then f is continuous on A.

(c) If f is continuous, then f is continuous on A, i.e., f_A is continuous.

Proof.   Let $p \in A$, and suppose f is continuous at p. Let U be a neighborhood of $f_A(p)$. Then, since f is continuous at p, there is a neighborhood V of p in X such that $f[V] \subset U$. Now $V \cap A$ is a neighborhood of p in the subspace A (see 4.2 in Ch 2). But

$$f_A[V \cap A] = f[V \cap A] \subset f[V] \subset U.$$

Therefore, by 1.1(a), f_A is continuous at p, and (a) is proved. Part (b) is immediate from (a), 1.1(b), and 2.1. Part (c) is a corollary of (b) since the continuity of f implies f is continuous at each point of A.

Example 2.3.   Let A be the set of all rational numbers, and let $f\colon\ R \longrightarrow R$ be defined by $f(x) = 0$ if $x \in A$ and $f(x) = 1$ if x is irrational.

Clearly this function f is not continuous at any point in R. However, the mapping f_A is continuous, i.e. (2.1), f is continuous on A. Also f is continuous on $R \sim A$. This example shows that f in 2.2 may be continuous on A even though f is not continuous at any point of A.

Theorem 2.4.   Let f and g be mappings of a space X into a T_2 space Y. If f and g are both continuous, then the set A of all x such that $f(x) = g(x)$ is a closed subset of X.

To prove this theorem, suppose $p \in X \sim A$ and show that (since $f(p) \neq g(p)$ in the T_2 space) there is a neighborhood W of p such that $W \subset X \sim A$ (i.e., if $x \in W$, then $f(x) \neq g(x)$).

Two mappings f and g of X into Y are said to agree on a subset B of X iff $f(x) = g(x)$ for each x in B.

Corollary 2.5.   Let f and g be continuous mappings of a space X into a T_2 space Y. If f and g agree on a dense subset B of X, then $f = g$, i.e., $f(x) = g(x)$ for each x in X.

A mapping $f \colon \ X \longrightarrow Y$ is called an extension of a mapping $g \colon \ A \longrightarrow Y$ where $A \subset X$ iff g is the restriction mapping f_A.

In view of 2.5, a function $f \colon \ B \longrightarrow Y$, where B is a dense subset of a space X and Y is a T_2 space, has at most one continuous extension mapping of X into Y.

3. Invariants Under Continuous Mappings

Let f be a continuous mapping of a connected space X onto a space Y. Then Y is connected. For suppose Y were not connected. Then, by 5.3 in Ch 2, there is a proper subset H of Y such that H is both open and closed. Now, by 1.4, $f^{-1}[H]$ is both open and closed in X. Also, since f is onto Y, $f^{-1}[H]$ is a proper subset of X. But this is impossible since X is connected. We conclude that Y is connected.

The proof of our next theorem follows the pattern of the above paragraph.

Theorem 3.1.   Let f be a mapping of a space X into a space Y, and let A be a connected subset of X. If f is continuous on A, then $f[A]$ is connected.

Proof. Suppose $f[A]$ is not connected. Then there is a proper subset H of $f[A]$ which is both open and closed in $f[A]$. Then (by 4.2 in Ch 2) there is an open subset U of Y such that $H = U \cap f[A]$, and (by 1(b) in 4.6 of Ch 2) there is a closed subset T of Y such that $H = T \cap f[A]$. Now, since f_A is continuous, $f_A^{-1}[U]$ is open in A and $f_A^{-1}[T]$ is closed in A. But

$$f_A^{-1}[U] = f_A^{-1}[H] = f_A^{-1}[T],$$

so that $f_A^{-1}[H]$ is both open and closed in A. Also, $f_A^{-1}[H]$ is a proper subset of A. Hence A is not connected, and 3.1 is proved.

The preceding theorem may be stated: A continuous image of a connected set is connected. We now apply this theorem to a real function of a real variable and obtain an important corollary which you have used many times, beginning in your freshman courses. Let f be a real function of a real variable which is continuous on a closed interval A from a to b. The set A is connected (Ch 2, 6.5). Hence, by 3.1, $f[A]$ is connected. Let c be any real number between $f(a)$ and $f(b)$. Now $f(a), f(b) \in f[A]$, and by 6.2 in Ch 2, $c \in f[A]$, i.e., there is some x in A such that $f(x) = c$. Thus:

Corollary 3.2. Let f be a real function of a real variable which is continuous on a closed interval from a to b. Then for each c in R between $f(a)$ and $f(b)$, there is an x between a and b such that $f(x) = c$.

Of course, from 3.2, we have the corollary: If, in 3.2, $f(a)$ and $f(b)$ have opposite signs, then there is an x between a and b such that $f(x) = 0$.

A property of a space is called an *invariant under continuous mappings* (or is said to be *invariant under continuous mappings*) iff whenever a space X has the property, then each continuous image of X has the property. So connectedness is invariant under continuous mappings. Another important property which is invariant under continuous mappings is that of being compact, which we now define.

Definition 3.3. (a) A subset A of a space X is *compact* iff each open cover for A has a finite subcover for A.

(b) A subset A of a space X is *countably compact* iff each infinite subset of A has a limit point in A. (In particular, the space X is compact or countably compact iff the subset X of the space X has the respective property.)

Here is an important, but simple, theorem for you to prove:

Theorem 3.4. Let f be a continuous mapping of a space X into a space Y. If A is a compact subset of X, then $f[A]$ is a compact subset of Y.

Definition 3.5. A subset A of X, where (X, d) is a metric space, is said to be *bounded* (*relative to* d) iff there is a real number r such that $d(x, y) < r$ for each pair x, y in A.

Exercises 3.6

1. Prove:

(a) A closed subset of a compact set is compact.

(b) A closed subset of a countably compact set is countably compact. (After working for a reasonable time on part (a), recall your proof of 1 in 3.9 of Ch 2, and use a similar argument for (a).)

2. (a) Prove: Each compact subset of a T_2 space is closed.

   (b) Give an example of a compact set which is not closed.

3. Prove: Each compact subset of a metric space is closed and bounded.

4. (a) Give an example of a closed and bounded subset A of a metric space X such that A is not compact.

   (b) Give an example of a continuous mapping f of a metric space X into a metric space Y and a closed and bounded subset A of X such that $f[A]$ is not closed and bounded.

5. Does there exist a continuous mapping of R onto the set of rationals with the relative topology of R?

6. Prove: A space X is connected iff there does not exist a continuous mapping f of X into R such that $f[X] = \{0, 1\}$.

Proof of 2(a). Let A be a compact subset of a T_2 space X, and suppose $p \in X \sim A$. (We shall show $p \notin A'$.) Since X is a T_2 space, for each x in A, there are disjoint neighborhoods U_x of x and V_x of p. Now $\{U_x : x \in A\}$ is an open cover for A; and, since A is compact, there is a finite subcover, say $\{U_a, U_b, \ldots, U_k\}$ (assuming $A \neq \varnothing$), for A. The set

$$V_a \cap V_b \cap \ldots \cap V_k$$

is a neighborhood of p which contains no point of A. Therefore $p \notin A'$ and A is closed.

For 2(b), let p be a point of an infinite set X with the finite complement topology. The set $X \sim \{p\}$ is compact but not closed.

One part of 3 follows from 2(a) (see 2 in 7.5 of Ch 2). The other part is left for your pleasure and experience.

One example for 4(a) may be obtained by taking the space X to be the set $I = \{x : x \in R, 0 < x < 1\}$ with the metric defined by $d(x, y) = |x - y|$ for $x, y \in I$. If $A = I$, then A is certainly closed and bounded. Show that A is not compact by giving an open cover for A which has no finite subcover for A.

Another example for 4(a) may be obtained by taking X and A the same as before but letting $d(x, y) = 1$ if $x \neq y$ and $d(x, y) = 0$ if $x = y$ for $x, y \in X$.

An example for 4(b) may be obtained by using either of the metrics mentioned for the set X used for 4(a). The mapping $f \colon X \longrightarrow R$ defined by $f(x) = 1/x$ is continuous relative to either of the two metrics mentioned for X, and $f[A]$ is not bounded where $A = X = I$.

4. Homeomorphisms

Definition 4.1. A mapping f of a space X into a space Y is called an *open mapping* iff U is open in X implies $f[U]$ is open in Y. Also, f is said to be *closed* iff H is closed in X implies $f[H]$ is closed in Y.

Remark 4.2. Let $f\colon X \longrightarrow Y$ be a one-to-one mapping of a space X onto a space Y. Then f is continuous iff the inverse mapping $f^{-1}\colon Y \longrightarrow X$ (as defined in 3.8 of Ch 1) is an open mapping.

This remark follows from 1.4(a) and (d). (Of course, we do not have an inverse mapping f^{-1} unless f is one-to-one; however, we do use the notation $f^{-1}[B]$ to denote $\{x\colon f(x) \in B\}$ where $B \subset Y$.)

Definition 4.3. (a) A mapping f of a space X onto a space Y is a *homeomorphism* iff f is one-to-one and continuous and f^{-1} is continuous.

(b) A space X is *homeomorphic* to a space Y iff there is a homeomorphism of X onto Y.

Theorem 4.4. Let f be a mapping of a space X onto a space Y. Then f is a homeomorphism iff f is one-to-one, continuous and open.

To prove this theorem, simply notice that $(f^{-1})^{-1} = f$, and apply 4.2 to the mapping f^{-1}—thus obtaining: f^{-1} is continuous iff f is open.

Theorem 4.4 is convenient in proving our next theorem, especially the (c) part. For (c) also use 5(b) in 1.6.

Theorem 4.5. Let X, Y and Z be spaces.

(a) The space X is homeomorphic to X.

(b) If X is homeomorphic to Y, then Y is homeomorphic to X.

(c) If X is homeomorphic to Y and Y is homeomorphic to Z, then X is homeomorphic to Z.

We see from 4.4 that a homeomorphism f of X onto Y not only establishes a one-to-one correspondence between the points of X and the points of Y, but also sets up a one-to-one correspondence between the open sets in X and the open sets in Y (because f is *both open and continuous*). Thus if X is homeomorphic to Y, then (topologically speaking) X and Y are "of the same form", and we see why the following definition is adopted.

Definition 4.6.   Two spaces X and Y are said to be *topologically equivalent* iff X is homeomorphic to Y.

We also see why it was of interest to observe in 4.5 that the relation "is homeomorphic to" is an equivalence relation.   Because of 4.5(b), we may use the expression "X and Y are homeomorphic" to mean "X is homeomorphic to Y", and in this case we call either space a *homeomorph* of the other. A homeomorphism is also called a *homeomorphic mapping*, a *topological mapping*, a *topological map*, or a *topological transformation*.   We should say that, in general, the following terms are often used synonymously: "function", "mapping", "map", and "transformation".

Definition 4.7.   A property of a space is said to be a *topological property* (or a *topological invariant*) iff a space X has the property implies each homeomorph of X has the property.

Of course, each invariant under continuous mappings is certainly invariant under homeomorphisms and hence is a topological property.

Example 4.8.   Let $X = \{x:\ x \in R$ and $3n - 3 < x < 3n - 2$ or $x = 3n - 1$ for $n \in N\}$, let $Y = \{1\} \cup X \sim \{2\}$, and let X and Y be subspaces of R with the usual topology. Let $f:\ X \longrightarrow Y$ and $g:\ Y \longrightarrow X$ be defined by

$$\text{for each } x \text{ in } X, \quad f(x) = \begin{cases} x & \text{if } x \neq 2 \\ 1 & \text{if } x = 2 \end{cases}$$

and

$$\text{for each } y \text{ in } Y, \quad g(y) = \begin{cases} y/2 & \text{if } y \leq 1 \\ y/2 - 1 & \text{if } 3 < y < 4 \\ y - 3 & \text{if } 5 \leq y. \end{cases}$$

Complete the following table to indicate which maps are continuous and which are open.

	$f:\ X \longrightarrow Y$	$g:\ Y \longrightarrow X$	$g \circ f:\ X \longrightarrow X$	$f \circ g:\ Y \longrightarrow Y$
continuous				
open				

We see that f is a one-to-one continuous map of X onto Y, and g is a one-to-one continuous map of Y onto X.   Yet, it is fairly easy to see that there is no homeomorphism of X onto Y.   For let h be any one-to-one map of X onto Y, and let $p \in X$ such that $h(p) = 1$.   If h is to be continuous, then p

must be one of the isolated points of the form $3n - 1$.   But then h is not open, since $\{p\}$ is open in X but $\{1\} = h[\{p\}]$ is not open in Y.

Exercises 4.9

1.   Let f be a one-to-one map of a space X onto a space Y.   Prove:

(a) f is a homeomorphism iff f is continuous and closed.   (Use 4.4.)

(b) f is a homeomorphism iff $f[A^-] = (f[A])^-$ for each subset A of X.   [Use part (a) and 1.4(a) and (f).]

2.   Let h be a homeomorphism of X onto Y, let $A \subset X$, and let $p \in X$. Prove $p \in A'$ iff $h(p) \in (h[A])'$.

3.   Show that each of the following properties is a topological property: the property of being a (a) T_2 space, (b) separable space, (c) countably compact space, (d) second countable space, (e) Lindelöf space.

4.   For each n in N let V_n be the open interval in R from $n - 1$ to n, let $X = \bigcup \{V_n : n \in N\}$, and let $\mathscr{T}$ be the topology for X which is generated by the family $\{V_n : n \in N\}$.   Prove that, with this topology, X is countably compact but not compact.

5.   Let $\mathscr{T}$ be the discrete topology for N, and let f be the map of the space $(X, \mathscr{T})$ in 4 onto the space $(N, \mathscr{T})$ defined as follows: For each x in X, let $f(x) = n$, where $n \in N$ and $n - 1 < x < n$.   Prove that f is continuous and N is not countably compact.   (Thus we see that a continuous image of a countably compact space need not be countably compact.   Compare this with 3(c) and 3.4.)   [However, 5 in 7.3 of Ch 4 shows that a continuous image of a countably compact T_1 space is countably compact.]

6.   Let f be a one-to-one continuous map of X onto Y.   Prove: If X is compact and Y is Hausdorff, then f is a homeomorphism.   [See 1(a) above, and show f is closed by using 1(a) in 3.6, 3.4, and 2(a) in 3.6.]   (In 4.8 we have several functions which are one-to-one and continuous but not open and hence not homeomorphisms.)

5.   Some Comments on Topology

We have stated earlier that a topological space is an abstraction of some of the important properties of the system of real numbers.   These "important properties" are primarily concerned with what we may roughly call "limit properties" (convergence, continuity, accumulation point); these properties may be described in terms of open sets. Actually, similar "limit properties" and the associated basic concepts are present in many areas of mathematics, including advanced calculus, n-dimensional geometry, functions of real variables, functions of complex variables, and other topics in modern analysis. In several branches of mathematics certain concepts, arguments, and methods are duplicated (sometimes in disguise).

Thus one would hope that the basic concepts underlying several areas of mathematics could be isolated and used as a basis upon which to build a general theory which contains as special cases many of the desired results in the specific areas. It would be hoped that such a general theory would not only be an economical way of obtaining many results, but would also help to clarify the various areas by pinpointing the properties upon which a given result rests.

During the last several decades, there has been a continual process (by mathematicians) of consolidating basic concepts and methods in analysis, abstracting on these, and extending them to more general settings. The results of some of these abstractions and generalizations constitute what we may call "general topology". So "general topology" is concerned with some of the basic concepts in analysis. Of course, "topology" is now a branch of mathematics which has attracted considerable attention for its own sake, and goes far beyond the basis for analysis; it includes "algebraic topology", which is not touched upon in this book at all.

The student may say of some of the ideas in our present work: "Yes, I find these ideas intriguing and especially pleasing when they explain in bare form some idea from an earlier mathematical experience—in calculus perhaps (such as convergence of a sequence or continuity of a function). But what about the other new ideas? Do they have very great significance other than intellectual intrigue?" He may be assured that almost every concept formally introduced in this book is a basic concept in modern analysis.

General topology has grown and taken shape after much experimentation on the part of the early researchers as they sought to determine the fruitful directions of abstraction. For example, one might try generalizing (from Euclidean spaces) to a semi-metric space, a pseudo-metric space, a metric space, or some other abstract system. As we have seen, a topological space may be considered as an abstraction of a metric space (since all metric spaces are special topological spaces). There is still another significant abstraction of the concept of a metric space, called a uniform space.

We have seen (in the last section of Ch 2) that there are several ways of formulating abstractions of a metric space to a topological space, some of which are logically equivalent; one uses "open set" as the basic notion, another uses "closed set" and still another uses "closure" as the basic concept, etc.

———————————

Perhaps, during this break from our "sequence" of theorems, it is appropriate that we discuss an axiom from set theory—the Axiom of Choice—which is frequently used in topology (as well as in other branches of mathematics). Without mentioning it, we have already used this axiom (or consequences of it) several times in our proofs. Consider the second sentence in the proof of 3.7 in Ch 2: "Select a point from each non-void member of $\mathcal{B}$, thus obtaining a . . . set A." Now in an intuitive sense, one might feel that it is reasonable to conclude that a perfectly good set A is obtained here. But in a formal system of mathematics, we realize that we do need an axiom to guarantee the existence of a set A obtained in such a manner. Or we may say that we need an axiom to assert that the above procedure is a valid way of "forming" a set A. One axiom which implies the existence of our set A is:

Zermelo's Postulate.   If $\mathcal{C}$ is a collection of non-void disjoint sets, then there is a subset A of $\bigcup \mathcal{C}$ such that, for each C in $\mathcal{C}$, $A \cap C$ consists of a single element.

There are several propositions each of which is logically equivalent to this postulate. At a glance, some of them seem to be equivalent, while others look drastically different. A few of these equivalent statements are: the Axiom of Choice, the Well-ordering Principle, Zorn's Lemma, Kuratowski's Lemma, and the Hausdorff Maximal Principle, which may be found in Ch 0 of Kelley's *General Topology* along with a few other equivalent statements. Because of such frequent references to it, we want to state the Choice Axiom here. The Hausdorff Maximal Principle is given in Ch 7.

Axiom of Choice.   If for each a in some set D, X_a is a non-void set, then there is a mapping f of D into $\bigcup \{X_a : a \in D\}$ such that $f(a) \in X_a$ for each a in D.

(Here the set D is just some set whose elements are used as subscripts in labeling the sets in our collection $\{X_a : a \in D\}$. When a set D is used for this purpose, it is called an *index set*. We could state the Axiom of Choice thusly: If $\mathcal{C}$ is a collection of non-null sets, then there is a mapping $f: \mathcal{C} \longrightarrow \bigcup \mathcal{C}$ such that $f(C) \in C$ for each C in $\mathcal{C}$. The mapping f is called a *choice function*.) [Usually, the Choice Axiom is stated for a non-void collection $\mathcal{C}$ of non-void sets. Since the null set of ordered pairs is (by our definition of function) a function on the null set C to the null set $\cup\, C$, the statement is valid when C is null. So I omitted the hypothesis of non-nullness of C.]

Now, if we wanted to be real stiff about the matter, we might replace the second sentence in our proof of 3.7 in Ch 2 by: "In view of the Axiom of Choice, let f be a choice function which 'chooses' an element from each non-void member of $\mathcal{B}$;   and let A be the range of f."

———————————

A system of axioms for a formal development of set theory includes several axioms in addition to the Axiom of Choice, some perhaps more subtle than this one.   But this is a book on topology—not axiomatic set theory.   So we do not give a set of axioms for such theory.   To be perfectly honest, so far as our mathematics is concerned, I feel there may be no greater need to make a fuss about the Choice Axiom than there is to state other axioms from set theory.   However, it is customary to cite this axiom in elementary courses in pure mathematics.   So I pass it on to you here—and free of charge.   I hope to have placed it in proper perspective by saying that there are other independent axioms in set theory, perhaps of equal importance.   You may see Halmos's little book, *Naive Set Theory* (listed at the end of Ch 1), which displays axioms for set theory.

Miscellaneous Exercises 5.1

As indicated in 1.3 of Ch 1, Q denotes $\{x:\ x \in R\ \text{ and }\ 0 \le x \le 1\}$.

1. Let $r \in R$, and let $B = Q \times \{r\}$ (i.e., B is the Cartesian product of Q and the singleton set $\{r\}$).   Prove that B is a connected subset of E_2. (*Hint*:   Observe that the mapping $f:\ Q \longrightarrow E_2$, defined by $f(q) = (q, r)$ for each q in Q, is continuous, and use 3.1.)   (Actually, f is a homeomorphism of Q onto B if B is taken as a subspace of E_2.)

2. For each n in N, let $B_n = Q \times \{1/n\}$, and let $X = \{(0, 0), (1, 0)\} \cup [\cup\, \{B_n:\ n \in N\}]$ with the relative topology of E_2 (where $(0, 0)$ and $(1, 0)$ are ordered pairs, not intervals).   Prove:

    (a) X is not locally connected ("at $(0, 0)$").

    (b) If H is open and closed in X, then H contains neither or both $(0, 0)$ and $(1, 0)$.

    (c) When $X = A \cup C$, where A and C are separated, then $(0, 0)$ and $(1, 0)$ belong to A or both belong to C.

3. A subset C of a space X is called a *component of X* iff C is a connected set which is not a subset of another connected set in X. Prove:

(a) Each connected set is contained in a component of the space. (See 1 in 5.8 of Ch 2.)

(b) Each component of a space is closed.   (Use 5.6 in Ch 2.)

(c) If A and B are different components of a space, then A and B are separated.   (1 in 5.8 of Ch 2.)

4. If two points p and q belong to the same component of a space X, then when $X = A \cup C$, where A and C are separated, both p and q must belong to A or $p, q \in C$.

5. Let X be the space in 2 above.

(a) What is the component of X which contains the point $(0, 0)$?

(b) What is the component of X which contains $(1, 0)$?

[The answers to questions (a) and (b) together with 2(c) show that the converse of 4 is not true.]

6. Let X be an uncountable set, and let p be some particular element of X.

(a) Let $\mathcal{T}$ be the family of subsets of X defined by: A subset G of X belongs to $\mathcal{T}$ iff $G = \varnothing$ or $p \in G$.   Show that $(X, \mathcal{T})$ is a separable space which has a subspace which is not separable.

(b) Let $\mathcal{F}$ be the family of subsets of X defined by: A subset G of X belongs to $\mathcal{F}$ iff $G = X$ or $p \notin G$.   Prove: $(X, \mathcal{F})$ is a Lindelöf space which has a subspace which is not Lindelöf.

[The spaces in (a) and (b) could be used in answering parts of 4 in 4.6 of Ch 2.   The space in (b) would have been a good one for the second part of 5 in 8.4 of Ch 2.]

7. Prove that each subspace of a second countable space is separable and Lindelöf.   [Recall that second countability is hereditary, and see 3.7 in Ch 2 and the last sentence before 3.9 in Ch 2.)

8. Let $f\colon Q \longrightarrow Q$ be a continuous map of the closed unit interval Q into Q.   Prove there is some c in Q such that $f(c) = c$.   [*Hint:* If $f(0) \neq 0$ and $f(1) \neq 1$, then let $g(x) = f(x) - x$ and apply 3.2 to the function g.]

4

Compactness

.

I. Conditions Related to Compactness

See 3.3 in Ch 3 for our definitions of a compact set and a countably compact set. These two concepts are important because the statement that a set is compact, or countably compact, has many useful implications. Perhaps the notion of compactness was first singled out and given a name because of a classical theorem of analysis—the Heine-Borel theorem for the system of real numbers. This theorem may be stated: A subset A of R is closed and bounded iff each open cover for A has a finite subcover for A. It also happens that another classical theorem states that a subset A of R is closed and bounded iff each infinite subset of A has a limit point in A. (We shall prove these two theorems soon.)

So before the general theories of topology were developed, it was known that there are many implications concerning a subset A of R which has any one of the three equivalent properties in R: (1) A is closed and bounded, (2) each infinite subset of A has a limit point in A, (3) each open cover for A has a finite subcover for A.

Now in the program of abstracting and generalizing (discussed at the end of Ch 3), one's first thought is that the boundedness part of property

76

(1) is meaningful only in a system which has a "distance function" such as a metric or pseudo-metric space. However, (2) and (3) are meaningful in any system in which limit point and open set are defined.

Early in the experimentation (of the generalizing process), property (2) was emphasized, and it was common for writers to say that a set A in a topological space is compact iff A has property (2) above. As we know (by 4 in 4.9 of Ch 3), in general spaces, (2) is not equivalent to (3). [Also, in metric spaces [4(a) in 3.6 of Ch 3], (1) is not equivalent to (3), while (2.6 in Ch 4), (2) and (3) are still equivalent in such spaces.] However (1.2 below), in any topological space, (3) implies (2). So (3) is the strongest of the three conditions and has the largest number of useful implications. Today, in the most widely adopted language, a set A is said to be compact iff each open cover for A has a finite subcover for A; and the term "countably compact" is now often used to mean what "compact" used to mean. [Because of the experimentation process and the freedom which people have in assigning names to concepts, there are many other terms in the mathematical literature which are used with different meanings by different people.]

In this book, we have adopted the language as given in 3.3 of Ch 3.

Theorem I.I.   Let A be a subset of a topological space. If each countable open cover for A has a finite subcover for A, then A is countably compact.

Proof. Suppose A is not countably compact. Then there is an infinite subset of A, say B, which has no limit point in A. Let H be a countable infinite subset of B. Then no point of A is a limit point of H (since $H' \subset B'$). Hence for each x in $A \sim H$, there is a neighborhood U_x of x such that $U_x \cap H = \varnothing$. Also, for each y in H (since $y \notin H'$), there is a neighborhood V_y of y such that $V_y \cap H = \{y\}$. The collection of all V_y for y in H together with the set $\bigcup \{U_x: \ x \in A \sim H\}$ is a countable open cover for A which certainly has no finite subcover for A and we have proved the contrapositive of 1.1.

Corollary I.2.   If A is a compact subset of a topological space, then A is countably compact.

Exercise 4 in 4.9 of Ch 3 shows that the converse of 1.2 is not valid. The space in the same exercise also shows that the converse of 1.1 is not true. (Give a countable open cover for this space which has no finite subcover for the space.)

If the blanket hypothesis in 1.1 is that A is a subset of a T_1 space, then the converse is true.

Theorem 1.3.   Let X be a countably compact T_1 space, and let $\mathcal{C}$ be a countable collection $\{U_1, U_2, U_3, \ldots\}$ of open subsets of X. If $\mathcal{C}$ covers X, then some finite subfamily of $\mathcal{C}$ covers X.

Proof. Suppose no finite subfamily of $\mathcal{C}$ covers X. Then for each n in N, the set A_n is non-void and closed where $A_n = X \sim \bigcup \{U_i : i \in N_n\}$. For each n in N, let $p_n \in A_n$; and let $P = \{p_n : n \in N\}$. (The set P exists by the Choice Axiom.)

Case I. Suppose P is infinite. Then (since X is countably compact) there is a point p in P'. Thus (9 in 1.18 of Ch 2) an arbitrary neighborhood V of p contains infinitely many points of P; and so, for a given k in N, V contains infinitely many points of $\{p_n : n > k\}$ which is a subset of the closed set A_k (since $A_n \subset A_k$ if $n > k$). Hence $p \in A_k'$ and so $p \in A_k$. Since k is arbitrary, it follows that $p \in A_n$ for each n in N. This means that $\mathcal{C}$ does not cover X.

Case II. Suppose P is finite. Then there is a point q in P such that, for each k in N, $p_i = q$ for some $i > k$ and so $q \in A_k$ (since $A_i \subset A_k$ if $i > k$). Thus, for each n in N, $q \in A_n$; and again $\mathcal{C}$ does not cover X.

We have shown that if no finite subfamily of $\mathcal{C}$ covers X, then $\mathcal{C}$ does not cover X—the contrapositive of 1.3.

See 4.3 in Ch 2 and verify the following remark.

Remark 1.4.   A subset A of a space X is a countably compact *subset* of X iff the *subspace* A is a countably compact space.

We now prove the following corollary of 1.3.

Corollary 1.5.   If A is a countably compact subset of a T_1 space X, then each countable open cover for A has a finite subcover for A.

Proof. By 1.4, the subspace A is countably compact. Also, A is a T_1 space. So, by 1.3, each countable cover for A with open subsets of the subspace A has a finite subcover for A. But each countable cover for A by open subsets of the space A has a finite subcover for A iff each countable cover for A by open subsets of X has a finite subcover for A (just see the definition of a subspace in 4.2 of Ch 2), and 1.5 is proved.

Combining 1.1 and 1.5, we now have:

Theorem 1.6.   A subset A of a T_1 space is countably compact iff each countable open cover for A has a finite subcover for A.

Theorems 1.1 and 1.6 serve as a good justification for using the term "countably compact" as we do (in Def 3.3 in Ch 3). (Some writers call a set A countably compact iff each countable open cover for A has a finite subcover for A. This definition is equivalent to our definition in T_1 spaces, but not in general.)

You should now enjoy putting together 3.8 of Ch 2, 1.5 and 1.2 to obtain:

Theorem 1.7 (Borel-Lebesgue).   A subset A of a second countable T_1 space is compact iff A is countably compact.

It is important to notice a companion theorem of 1.4 for compactness. See the definition of a subspace (4.2 in Ch 2) and prove:

Remark 1.8.   A subset A of a space X is a compact *subset* of X iff A is a compact *subspace* of X.

Definition 1.9.   A family $\mathcal{F}$ of sets has the *finite intersection property* (abbreviated FIP) iff each finite subfamily of $\mathcal{F}$ has a non-null intersection.

Theorem 1.10.   A space X is compact iff each family of closed subsets of X with the FIP has a non-null intersection.

Proof. Suppose X is compact, and let $\mathcal{F}$ be a family of closed subsets of X with the FIP. Then $\{X \sim F: F \in \mathcal{F}\}$ is a collection of open sets, no finite subfamily of which covers X. [For let

$$\{X \sim F_1, X \sim F_2, \ldots, X \sim F_n\}$$

be *any* non-void finite subfamily of this collection. By a DeMorgan formula,

$$X \sim \bigcup \{X \sim F_1, X \sim F_2, \ldots, X \sim F_n\} = \bigcap \{F_1, F_2, \ldots, F_n\} \neq \varnothing$$

(since $\mathcal{F}$ has the FIP).] Hence $\{X \sim F: F \in \mathcal{F}\}$ does not cover X (since X is compact). Therefore

$$\bigcap \mathcal{F} \neq \varnothing, \quad \text{since} \quad \bigcap \mathcal{F} = X \sim \bigcup \{X \sim F: F \in \mathcal{F}\}.$$

To prove the converse, suppose that each family of closed sets with the FIP has a non-void intersection, and let $\mathcal{C}$ be an open cover for X. Then $\{X \sim C: C \in \mathcal{C}\}$ is a family of closed sets with a null intersection (by a DeMorgan formula). Hence some finite subfamily, say

$$\{X \sim C_1, X \sim C_2, \ldots, X \sim C_n\},$$

has a void intersection; and

$$\bigcup \{C_1, C_2, \ldots, C_n\} = X \sim \bigcap \{X \sim C_i: i = 1, 2, 3, \ldots, n\} = X.$$

Therefore X is compact, and 1.10 is proved.

Let us say that a family $\mathcal{C}$ of subsets of a space X is *short* iff $\mathcal{C}$ does not cover X, and let us say that $\mathcal{C}$ is *finitely short* iff no finite subfamily of $\mathcal{C}$ covers X. Also, let us say that $\mathcal{C}$ is *common* iff $\bigcap \mathcal{C} \neq \varnothing$ and that $\mathcal{C}$ is *finitely common* iff each finite subfamily of $\mathcal{C}$ has a non-void intersection. Our definition of compactness of a space translated into this present language gives:

Remark 1.11.   A space X is compact iff

(a) each finitely short family of open sets in X is short.

Let $\mathcal{F}$ be a family of subsets of a space X and let $\mathcal{F}^\frown$ be the family $\{X \sim F: \ F \in \mathcal{F}\}$. It is clear that

(1) $\mathcal{F}$ is a family of open sets iff $\mathcal{F}^\frown$ is a family of closed sets.

Also using the DeMorgan formulae:

(2) $\mathcal{F}$ is short iff $\mathcal{F}^\frown$ is common, and

(3) $\mathcal{F}$ is finitely short iff $\mathcal{F}^\frown$ is finitely common.

We now see that (in view of the above equivalences) condition (a) in 1.11 is equivalent to

(b) each finitely common family of closed subsets of X is common.

Since, by 1.11, (a) is equivalent to the compactness of X, it follows that (b) is equivalent to the compactness of X. If we had practiced in the above mental gymnastics with families of sets, we could have said that the result in 1.10 is clear without proof. Since we have already proved 1.10, there is no need to worry about the above gymnastics. However, I believe that to consider them would be good; and having done so, we may say it is clear from 1.6 that:

Remark 1.12.   A T_1 space X is countably compact iff each countable family of closed sets in X with the FIP has a non-void intersection.

(If you do not wish to practice the above mentioned gymnastics until 1.12 is clear, you may use 1.6 and a proof similar to that of 1.10 to obtain 1.12.)

Corollary 1.13 (Cantor Theorem).   Let $\{C_1, C_2, C_3, \ldots\}$ be a monotone decreasing countable family of non-void closed subsets of a T_1 space such that C_1 is countably compact. Then $\bigcap \{C_i: \ i \in N\} \neq \varnothing$.

You are now familiar with the technique of considering the (countably compact T_1) subspace C_1 in giving an argument to establish 1.13.

Exercises I.14

1. Let I be the open interval from 0 to 1 in the space R.

    (a) Prove that I is not countably compact. [Hence (by 1.2) I is not compact, as we already knew from 5 in 3.6 of Ch 3.]

    (b) Give a family of closed subsets of the subspace I with the FIP which has a void intersection.

    (c) Give a family of closed subsets of R with the FIP which has a null intersection.

    (d) Give an open cover for R which has no finite subcover for R.

2. Prove that if A is an open interval in R, then A is not countably compact (and hence not compact).

3. Prove: Each finite subset of any topological space is compact. (Is each finite set in a space countably compact?)

4. Let $\mathcal{C}$ be a non-void collection of closed compact subsets of a space. Prove: $\cap \mathcal{C}$ is compact. [Use 1.6(a) in Ch 2 and 1(a) in 3.6 of Ch 3.]

5. Give an example of two compact subsets A and B of a space such that $A \cap B$ is not compact.

A solution to 5. Let X be an infinite set, let $p, q \in X$ with $p \neq q$, and let a subset G of X be open iff $G = X$ or $G \cap \{p, q\} = \varnothing$. Let $A = X \sim \{p\}$, and let $B = X \sim \{q\}$.

2. Compact Metric Spaces

Definition 2.1.   A metric space (X, d) is *totally bounded* iff for each real number $\epsilon > 0$, there is a finite subset F of X such that $\{S_\epsilon(p): \ p \in F\}$ covers X.

Theorem 2.2.   Each countably compact metric space (X, d) is totally bounded.

Proof. Suppose there were some $\epsilon > 0$ for which the desired finite set F does not exist. Let $p_1 \in X$. By our supposition, $\{S_\epsilon(p_1)\}$ does not cover

X. So let $p_2 \in X$ such that $d(p_1, p_2) \geq \epsilon$. Since $\{S_\epsilon(p_1), S_\epsilon(p_2)\}$ does not cover X, we may let $p_3 \in X$ such that $d(p_1, p_3) \geq \epsilon$ and $d(p_2, p_3) \geq \epsilon$. Suppose for some n in N,

$$\{p_1, p_2, p_3, \ldots, p_n\} \subset X$$

such that $d(p_i, p_j) \geq \epsilon$ for i, j in N_n with $i \neq j$. By our supposition,

$$\{S_\epsilon(p_i): \quad i = 1, 2, 3, \ldots, n\}$$

does not cover X. So let $p_{n+1} \in X$ such that

$$d(p_i, p_{n+1}) \geq \epsilon \qquad \text{for } i = 1, 2, 3, \ldots, n.$$

By induction, for each m in N, there is a point p_m in X such that $d(p_i, p_j) \geq \epsilon$ for each i, j in N with $i \neq j$. Because X is countably compact, there is a point p in X which is a limit point of the infinite set $\{p_m: \ m \in N\}$. This implies that the $\epsilon/2$-neighborhood about p contains *infinitely* many points in $\{p_m: \ m \in N\}$ (since X is T_1). (Use the triangle inequality to show that $d(p, p_i) < \epsilon/2$ and $d(p, p_j) < \epsilon/2$ implies $d(p_i, p_j) < \epsilon$. With $i \neq j$, this is a contradiction.) So we must reject our original supposition and conclude that X is totally bounded.

Theorem 2.3.   Each countably compact metric space (X, d) is separable.

Proof. In view of 2.2, for each n_0 in N, let F_{n_0} be a finite subset of X such that $\{S_r(p): \ p \in F_{n_0}\}$, where $r = 1/n_0$ covers X. (So if $x \in X$ and $n \in N$, then the $1/n$-sphere about x contains at least one point in F_n.) Let $H = \bigcup \{F_n: \ n \in N\}$. H is countable, and $H^- = X$. (To show $H^- = X$, see 7.7(b) in Ch 2, suppose $x \in X$, and let $\epsilon > 0$. Let $k \in N$ such that $1/k < \epsilon$. Since $S_{1/k}(x)$ contains at least one point in F_k, it follows that $S_\epsilon(x)$ contains at least one point of F_k and hence a point of H. Therefore $x \in H^-$ and $H^- = X$.)

Theorem 2.4.   A metric space (X, d) is separable iff it is second countable.

Proof. The if part is covered by 3.7 in Ch 2. So suppose X is separable, and let H be a countable set which is dense in X. Let

$$\mathcal{C} = \{S_r(p): \ p \in H \text{ and } r \text{ is a positive rational number}\} \quad (r \text{ is not fixed}).$$

Show that $\mathcal{C}$ is a countable base for the metric topology. [To see that $\mathcal{C}$ is a base, suppose $q \in U \subset X$, where U is open. By 5 in 7.5 of Ch 2, let $r > 0$ such that $S_r(q) \subset U$, and let t be a rational number such that $0 < t < r/2$. Since $H^- = X$, there is some x in H such that $d(x, q) < t$. Now $S_t(x) \in \mathcal{C}$, and $q \in S_t(x) \subset S_r(q) \subset U$. (For if $z \in S_t(x)$, then

$$d(q, z) \leq d(q, x) + d(x, z) < t + t < r.)$$

Thus $\mathcal{C}$ is a base for the metric topology.]

We are now in a position to prove that in a metric space, a set is compact iff it is countably compact.

Theorem 2.5.   A metric space (X, d) is countably compact iff it is compact.

Proof.   The if part is covered by 1.2.   Suppose X is countably compact. Then, by 2.3, X is separable;   and, by 2.4, X is second countable.   Since X is a T_1 space, we conclude from 1.7 that X is compact, and 2.5 is proved.

You are familiar with the technique of using subspaces to conclude that a subset A of a metric space is countably compact iff A is compact.   However, some of the details are recorded here.   Let (X, d) be a metric space, and let $A \subset X$.   (Recall that d is a map of $X \times X$ into R.)   If e is the restriction map of d to $A \times A$, then clearly (A, e) is a metric space.   It can be seen that the e-metric topology for A is identical with the relativization to A of the d-metric topology for X.   So, when we refer to the subspace A, we may use e to induce the topology for A if we like.   Now, in view of 1.4 and 1.8, we have from 2.5:

Theorem 2.6.   A subset A of a metric space is countably compact iff A is compact.

Perhaps we should style theorem 2.2 for subsets also.   We say that a subset A of a metric space (X, d) is *totally bounded* iff the metric subspace (A, e) is totally bounded where e is the restriction of d to $A \times A$.   We now use 2.2 (and 1.4—and the fact that the metric subspace (A, e) is the same topological space as the subspace A of X obtained by using the relativized d-topology) to conclude:

Theorem 2.7.   If A is a countably compact subset of a metric space, then A is totally bounded.

[According to our definitions (just before 2.7 and in 2.1), the conclusion in 2.7 means: For each $\epsilon > 0$, there is a finite set of points *in* A, say F, such that $\{S_\epsilon(p): \ p \in F\}$ covers A.]

Exercises 2.8

1. Give an example of a metric space which is not separable and hence, by 2.3, not countably compact.

2. Give an example of a separable metric space which is not countably compact.   (So the converse of 2.3 is not true.)

3. Uniform Continuity

Definition 3.1.   Let f be a map of a metric space (X, d) into a metric space (Y, e). Then f is said to be *uniformly continuous* iff for each $\epsilon > 0$, there is a $\delta > 0$ such that $e(f(x), f(y)) < \epsilon$ whenever $x, y \in X$ with $d(x, y) < \delta$. [f is said to be *uniformly continuous on A* where $A \subset X$ iff the restriction map f_A of the metric subspace A into Y is uniformly continuous.]

See 2.1 in Ch 6 for the definition of "diameter of a set".

Remark α.   Let (X, d) be a compact metric space, and let $\mathcal{C}$ be an open cover for X. There is a $\delta > 0$ (called a *Lebesgue number of* $\mathcal{C}$) such that each subset of X of diameter $< \delta$ is contained in some member of $\mathcal{C}$.

Proof. Suppose α is false. Then for each n in N, there is a subset A_n of X of diameter $< 1/n$ and A_n is contained in no member of $\mathcal{C}$. For each n in N, let $p_n \in A_n$. Since X is compact, let $p \in X$ such that $p_i \in U$ for infinitely many i's, where U is any neighborhood of p. Let $G \in \mathcal{C}$ such that $p \in G$. Let $r > 0$ such that the sphere $S_r(p) \subset G$.
Let $k \in N$ such that $1/k < r/2$ and such that $p_k \in S_{r/2}(p)$. If $y \in A_k$, then

$$ d(p, y) \le d(p, p_k) + d(p_k, y) < \frac{r}{2} + \frac{1}{k} < \frac{r}{2} + \frac{r}{2}. $$

Hence $A_k \subset S_r(p) \subset G$—a contradiction.

Theorem 3.2.   Let f be a map of a metric space (X, d) into a metric space (Y, e). If f is continuous and X is compact, then f is uniformly continuous.

Proof. [Be sure to use α to give your own proof first.] Let $\epsilon > 0$. Then $\{f^{-1}[S_{\epsilon/2}(q)]: \ q \in Y\}$ is an open cover for X. Let δ be a Lebesgue number of this cover. An application of the triangle inequality will show that if $d(x, y) < \delta$ then $e(f(x), f(y)) < \epsilon$.

Exercises 3.3

1. Let f be a map of a metric space X into a metric space Y.

(a) Prove: If f is uniformly continuous, then f is continuous (i.e., f is continuous at each point of X).

(b) Observe the distinction between continuity of f and uniform continuity of f.

2. Let $I(= \{x: \quad x \in R \quad \text{and} \quad 0 < x < 1\})$ be a metric subspace of R. Let $f: \quad I \longrightarrow R$ be the map defined by $f(x) = 1/x$ for each x in I. Prove that f is continuous but not uniformly continuous.

4. Compact Subsets of R

Since one of our objectives in this study of topology (in addition to providing background for further study in modern mathematics) is to enhance the study of advanced calculus and function theory, I consider our applications to the space of reals to be some of the highlights of our project; I also regard these applications as highlights because properties of the reals originally led to the abstract concepts in this book.

So fanfare is in order at the beginning of this section and just before our first theorem, which quickly gives us one half of the Heine-Borel Theorem for R—a very important theorem in real analysis. I believe the best fanfare here (which might turn out to be slightly prolonged) would be an attempt by the student to prove the classic result: Each open cover for a closed interval in R has a finite subcover for the closed interval. (In the proof, you might expect to use some basic property of R such as 6.1 in Ch 2.)

Theorem 4.1. Let $a, b \in R$ with $a < b$, and let A be the closed interval from a to b. The set A is compact.

Proof. (We use the notation for intervals explained in 11 of 8.4 in Ch 2.) Let C be an open cover for A. Let $B = \{x: \quad x \in A$ and some finite subfamily of C covers the closed interval $[a, x]\}$. Now $B \neq \varnothing$. (For $a \in U$ for some U in C, and the open set U must contain an open interval G about a. Certainly all points in $G \cap (a, b]$ belong to B.) Also, b is an upper bound for B. By 6.1 in Ch 2, let $s = \sup B$. Clearly $a < s \leq b$, and so $s \in A$. Hence $s \in V$ for some V in C. There is some open interval H such that $s \in H \subset V$.

Now let $r \in H$ such that $a < r < s$. Then $r \in B$, and there is a finite subfamily of C, say $\{W_1, W_2, \ldots, W_n\}$, which covers $[a, r]$. Then $\{V, W_1, W_2, \ldots, W_n\}$ covers $[a, s]$ and hence $s \in B$. Further, if s were less than b, there would be some t in H such that $s < t < b$, and $\{V, W_1, W_2, \ldots, W_n\}$ would cover $[a, t]$, so that $t \in B$ in contradiction to the fact that $s - \sup B$. Hence $b = s \in B$. By the definition of B, this means some finite subfamily of C covers A. Hence A is compact.

Put some of our previous results together to obtain your own proof of:

Theorem 4.2 (Heine-Borel Theorem for R). A subset B of R is compact iff B is closed and bounded.

Proof. The only if part is covered by 3 in 3.6 of Ch 3. To prove the other half, suppose B is closed and bounded. Then there is some closed interval A such that $B \subset A$. Hence B is compact by 4.1 above and 1(a) in 3.6 of Ch 3.

See 1.7 and conclude:

Theorem 4.3 (Bolzano-Weierstrass).   A subset A of R is countably compact iff A is closed and bounded.

Remark 4.4.   Let $A \subset R$ such that A has a supremum in R, and let $s = \sup A$.   (a) Then $s \in A^-$.   (b) If A is closed, then $s \in A$.

Proofs of the following interesting results are left for you.

Theorem 4.5.   Let A be a closed interval in R, and let f be a continuous map of A into R.   Then:

(a) The set $f[A]$ is closed and bounded.

(b) There is some p in A such that $f(p) = \sup f[A]$.

(c) The map f is uniformly continuous.

Compare these results with 2 in 3.3.   Result (b) is sometimes expressed by saying that a continuous real-valued function on a closed interval in R takes on (or attains or assumes) a maximum value.

A function f: $X \longrightarrow R$ (where X is any domain) is said to be *bounded* iff there is some real number r such that, for each x in X, $|f(x)| < r$.   This is equivalent to the condition that the set $f[X]$ is bounded in R.   We conclude that if X is compact and f is continuous, then f is bounded.   The map f in 2 of 3.3 is not bounded.   Give an example of a continuous map g: $I \longrightarrow R$ which is bounded but which does not take on a maximum (where I is the same as in 2 of 3.3).

Exercises 4.6

1. Let S be a bounded monotone non-decreasing sequence in R.   Prove that S converges to some real number.   (By *bounded*, we mean there is some r in R such that, for each n in N, $|S_n| < r$.   By *monotone non-decreasing*, we mean $S_n \leq S_m$ if $n < m$.)

2. Let A be a closed interval in R, and let f: $A \longrightarrow R$ be a continuous map.   Prove: there is some c in A such that, for each x in A, $f(c) \leq f(x)$.

5. Separation Properties

Definition 5.1.   Let $(X, \mathscr{T})$ be a topological space.

(a) X is said to be *regular* iff for each closed set A in X and each point p in $X \sim A$, there are disjoint open sets U and V such that $A \subset U$ and $p \in V$.

(b) X is *normal* iff for each pair of disjoint closed sets A and B in X, there are disjoint open sets U and V such that $A \subset U$ and $B \subset V$.

(c) X is *completely normal* iff for each pair of separated sets A and B in in X, there are disjoint open sets U and V such that $A \subset U$ and $B \subset V$.

In this section, we would like to make several general observations, and return to compact sets in the next section.

First, let us recall the definition of a T_2 space [1.17(d) in Ch 2] and the condition in 8 of 1.18 in Ch 2, which is equivalent to the property of being a T_1 space. [This condition in 8 of 1.18 in Ch 2 is often used as the defining property of a T_1 space; our definition is in 1.17(c) of Ch 2.] Next, let us add a further definition which fits into the picture.

Definition 5.2.   A space X is a T_0 *space* iff for each pair of distinct points in X, there is a neighborhood of at least one of these points which does not contain the other point.

[Compare the condition in 5.2 with the one in 8 of 1.18 in Ch 2. Note that the one in 8 of 1.18 in Ch 2 means: For each pair of distinct points in X, there is a neighborhood of each point which does not contain the other— for either point could be named x.]

Exercises 5.3

1. Give an example of a topological space which is (a) not a T_0 space, (b) a T_0 but not a T_1 space.

2. After doing 1, consider the space in 3 of 8.4 in Ch 2.

   (a) Will this space serve the purpose for 1(b) above?

   (b) Prove this space $(R, \mathscr{F})$ is normal.

   [*Hint:* Specify the closed subsets of this space.]

3. Prove: Each T_1 space is a T_0 space.

We see [3 above and 11 in 1.18 of Ch 2] that: A space is T_i implies it is T_{i-1} for $i = 1, 2$.   But [1(b) above and 13(b) in 1.18 of Ch 2] for $i = 0, 1$ there are spaces which are T_i but not T_{i+1}.   So the T_i conditions, $i = 0, 1, 2$, are indeed successively stronger.

One might now ask if the conditions in 5.1 are successively stronger, and if each is stronger than the T_2 condition.   An indiscrete space with more than one point serves to show that no one of the conditions in 5.1 implies T_2-ness.   However, if we consider only spaces which are T_1 (each singleton set is closed), the situation is different.   Clearly each T_1 regular space is T_2 [for the closed set A in (a) of 5.1 may be taken to be the singleton set $\{q\}$ in the T_1 space, where $q \neq p$];   similarly one of the closed sets in (b) of 5.1 may be taken to be a singleton set in a T_1 space to give the result that each T_1 normal space is regular.   Before stating these results formally, we would like to state a remark for you to prove, and then to state some more definitions.

Remark 5.4.   Each completely normal space is normal.

Definition 5.5.   (a) A space X is a T_3 *space* iff it is T_1 and regular.

(b) A space X is a T_4 *space* iff it is T_1 and normal.

(c) A space X is a T_5 *space* iff it is T_1 and completely normal.

Remark 5.6.   Each T_i space is a T_{i-1} space for $i = 1, 2, 3, 4, 5$.

[Each case in 5.6 has already been covered by a formal exercise or remark except for $i = 3$ and $i = 4$.   Write formal proofs for these two cases, using the appropriate singleton sets as suggested in the last paragraph before 5.4.]

Examples 5.7.   (a)   *A T_2 space which is not T_3.*   Let $\mathcal{U}$ be the usual topology for R, and let Y be the set of all rational numbers.   Let $\mathscr{T}$ be the family of subsets of R defined by: A subset G of R belongs to $\mathscr{T}$ iff for each point p in G, there is a $\mathcal{U}$-open interval A in R such that $p \in A$ and $A \cap Y \subset G$.   [Clearly $(R, \mathscr{T})$ is a T_2 space.   Let $B = R \sim Y$ and let $r \in Y$. Clearly B is $\mathscr{T}$-closed.   But there do not exist disjoint $\mathscr{T}$-open sets about B and r.   For let V be any $\mathscr{T}$-open set containing r.   Then there is a $\mathcal{U}$-open interval A in R such that $r \in A$ and $A \cap Y \subset V$.   Now there is an irrational number b in A.   So any $\mathscr{T}$-open set containing b must contain points of V. Thus $(R, \mathscr{T})$ is not regular.   Further (since $(R, \mathscr{T})$ is T_1) this space is not normal (by 5.6).]

(b) *Another T_2 space which is not T_3.*   Let A be the set of all points in E_2 "above the x-axis" (i.e., $A = \{(x, y): x, y \in R \text{ and } y > 0\}$), and let H be the "horizontal axis" ($H = \{(x, 0): x \in R\}$).   Let $X = A \cup H$, and let $\mathscr{B}$ be the family of subsets of X defined by: A subset G of X belongs to $\mathscr{B}$ iff

1. G is a sphere in E_2 with center (a, b) in A and radius $r < b$, or
2. $G = [S_r(p) \cap A] \cup \{p\}$, where $p \in H$ (and where all spheres are in E_2 with the standard metric).

Let $\mathscr{T}$ be the topology for X which has $\mathscr{B}$ as a base. Then $(X, \mathscr{T})$ is a T_2 space, but not regular and, of course, not normal. To see that $(X, \mathscr{T})$ is not regular, let $p \in H$ and let $B = H \sim \{p\}$. Then notice that B is closed and there are no disjoint open sets about B and p, respectively.

In 5.12, we describe a T_3 space which is not T_4, and there are T_4 spaces which are not T_5 spaces (3.3 in Ch 7). So the T_i conditions are successively stronger.

Exercise 5.8

Show that the space in 3 of 8.4 in Ch 2 is not regular. [But this space is normal by 2(b) in 5.3 of this section. So normality (in the absence of T_1-ness) does not imply regularity. (As already observed, indiscrete spaces show that) regularity does not imply T_2-ness.]

Theorem 5.9. (a) A space X is regular iff for each $p \in X$ and each neighborhood U of p, there is a neighborhood V of p such that $V^- \subset U$.

(b) If X is a regular space, A is a closed subset of X, and $p \in X \sim A$, then there are open sets U and W such that $A \subset U$, $p \in W$, and $U^- \cap W^- = \varnothing$.

Proof. (a) Suppose X is regular, $p \in X$, and U is a neighborhood of p. Then there are disjoint open sets V and W such that $p \in V$ and $X \sim U \subset W$, i.e., $U \supset X \sim W$. But $U \supset X \sim W \supset V$ (since V and W are disjoint). So $U \supset X \sim W \supset V^-$ (since $X \sim W$ is closed).

Now suppose the condition in (a) holds, A is a closed subset of X, and $p \in X \sim A$. By hypothesis, there is a neighborhood V of p such that $V^- \subset X \sim A$, i.e., $X \sim V^- \supset A$. So V and $X \sim V^-$ are the desired disjoint open sets, and X is regular.

(b) By regularity, there are disjoint open sets V and U (i.e., $U \subset X \sim V$ so that $U^- \subset X \sim V$) such that $p \in V$ and $A \subset U$. By (a), there is a neighborhood W of p such that $W^- \subset V$. So W^- and U^- are disjoint.

Theorem 5.10. (a) A space X is normal iff for each closed subset A of X and each open set U containing A, there is an open set V such that $A \subset V$ and $V^- \subset U$.

(b) If A and B are disjoint closed subsets of a normal space X, then there are open sets W and T with disjoint closures such that $A \subset W$ and $B \subset T$.

Exercises 5.11

1. Let (X, d) be a metric space, $p \in X$, and r a positive real number. Let $A = S_r(p)$.

    (a) Prove: If $q \in A^-$, then $d(p, q) \leq r$.

    (b) Construct an example to show that the converse of (a) is not true.

    (c) Prove: If $t > r$, then $A^- \subset S_t(p)$.

2. Prove: Each metric space is regular. [Use 5 in 7.5 of Ch 2, 5.9(a) and 1(c) above.]

Example 5.12.   Here is a T_3 space which is not T_4. We take the space in 5.7(b) just as it is, except that we replace condition 2 by

2'. $G = S_r(p) \cup \{(c, 0)\}$, where $p = (c, r)$.

So G (in 2') is the interior of a sphere in the "upper half" of E_2 which is "tangent to the x-axis" together with the point of tangency.

It is easy to see that this space is T_1 and regular [5.9(a)]. Also, the sets $B = \{(x, 0): \ x \text{ is irrational}\}$ and $D = \{(x, 0): \ x \text{ is rational}\}$ are disjoint closed sets. But there are no disjoint open sets about B and D—although a proof of this is not convenient to give at this stage.

6. Compactness and Separation Properties

Theorem 6.1.   Let A be a compact subset of a T_2 space X and let $p \in X \sim A$. Then there are disjoint open sets U and V such that $A \subset U$ and $p \in V$.

[After giving your own proof of 6.1, you might compare it with our proof of 2(a) in 3.6 of Ch 3. Note that we may obtain the desired open sets in 6.1 by taking $U = \bigcup \{U_a, U_b, \ldots, U_k\}$ and $V = \bigcap \{V_a, V_b, \ldots, V_k\}$ in that proof.]

Theorem 6.2.   If A and B are disjoint compact subsets of a T_2 space, then there are disjoint open sets U and V such that $A \subset U$ and $B \subset V$.

[A proof of 6.2 may rest upon 6.1. Have fun.]

Corollary 6.3. (a) Each compact T_2 space is normal (and, indeed, T_4).
(b) Each compact T_2 space is regular.

Theorem 6.4. If A is a compact subset of a regular space and U is an open set containing A, then there is an open set V such that $A \subset V$ and $V^- \subset U$.

Proof. For each p in A, let V_p be a neighborhood of p such that $V_p^- \subset U$ [5.9(a)]. Since A is compact, there is a finite subfamily of $\{V_p \colon \ p \in A\}$, say $\{V_a, V_b, \ldots, V_k\}$, which covers A. If we let $V = \bigcup \{V_a, V_b, \ldots, V_k\}$, then

$$A \subset V \quad \text{and} \quad V^- = \bigcup \{V_a^-, V_b^-, \ldots, V_k^-\} \subset U.$$

Theorem 6.5. If X is a regular Lindelöf space, then X is normal.

Proof. Let A and B be disjoint closed subsets of X. By 5.9(a), for each p in A, let V_p be a neighborhood of p such that $V_p^- \subset X \sim B$, i.e., $V_p^- \cap B = \varnothing$. By 1 in 3.9 of Ch 2, let $\{V_1, V_2, \ldots, V_n, \ldots\}$ be a countable subcover of $\{V_p \colon \ p \in A\}$ for A; so $V_i^- \cap B = \varnothing$ for each i in N. Similarly, let $\{U_1, U_2, \ldots, U_n, \ldots\}$ be a countable open cover for B such that $U_i^- \cap A = \varnothing$ for each i in N.
  For each n in N, let

$$W_n = V_n \sim \bigcup \{U_i^- \colon \ i \leq n\}$$

and

$$Z_n = U_n \sim \bigcup \{V_i^- \colon \ i \leq n\}.$$

Now $W_n \cap U_i = \varnothing$ if $i \leq n$, and $Z_i \subset U_i$; so $W_n \cap Z_i = \varnothing$ if $i \leq n$. Similarly, $Z_j \cap W_n = \varnothing$ if $n \leq j$. Hence $W_m \cap Z_k = \varnothing$ for each m, $k \in N$.
  By 5(a) in 1.18 of Ch 2, the sets W_n and Z_n are open for each n in N.
  Now recall that $\{V_n \colon \ n \in N\}$ was a cover for A and no U_i^- contains points of A. So $\{W_n \colon \ n \in N\}$ is an open cover for A. Also, $\{Z_n \colon \ n \in N\}$ is an open cover for B; and $\bigcup \{W_n \colon \ n \in N\}$ and $\bigcup \{Z_n \colon \ n \in N\}$ are disjoint open sets containing A and B respectively.

Since a compact space is certainly Lindelöf, the following statement is a direct corollary of 6.5:

Corollary 6.6. Each compact regular space is normal.

Also, since each second countable space is Lindelöf:

Corollary 6.7. Each second countable regular space is normal.

Exercises 6.8

1. Show how 6.6 follows as a corollary of 6.4.

2. (a) (Accepting the result that the space in 5.12 is not normal) is this space second countable?   (See 6.7.)

    (b) Show directly (using the fact that second countability is hereditary) that this space is not second countable.

3. (a) Are the spaces R and E_2 normal?

    (b) Is the space in 11(b) of 8.4 in Ch 2 normal?

7. One-point Compactification

Definition 7.1.   Let $(X, \mathcal{T})$ be a topological space, let p be an element which is not a member of the set X, and let $Y = X \cup \{p\}$.   Let $\mathcal{F}$ be the family of subsets of Y defined by: A subset G of Y belongs to $\mathcal{F}$ iff $G \in \mathcal{T}$ or $Y \sim G$ is a $\mathcal{T}$-closed $\mathcal{T}$-compact subset of X.   The pair $(Y, \mathcal{F})$ is called the *one-point compactification* of $(X, \mathcal{T})$.

Exercise 6 in 7.3 assures us that $\mathcal{F}$ in 7.1 is a topology for Y, that $(Y, \mathcal{F})$ is a compact space, and that $(X, \mathcal{T})$ is a subspace of $(Y, \mathcal{F})$.   So each space can be "compactified" in a useful way by adjoining a single point.

In the study of functions of a complex variable, it is the usual practice to adjoin a single point (denoted ∞) to the Euclidean plane E_2 and to topologize $E_2 \cup \{\infty\} = Z$ by saying that a subset G of Z is open iff G is an open subset of E_2 or $Z \sim G$ is a closed and bounded subset of E_2 [closedness and boundedness in E_2 being equivalent to compactness (2.2 in Ch 7)].   The resulting space is often called the complex sphere.   Thus the complex sphere is just the one-point compactification of E_2.

The space R is often compactified by adjoining two elements (denoted by ∞ and $-\infty$, respectively) and properly topologizing $R \cup \{-\infty, \infty\}$. The resulting space is often called the *extended reals* (though we call neither ∞ nor $-\infty$ a real number).   This is a compactification of R, but not the one-point compactification.   These compactifications are merely conveniences at times.

Definition 7.2.   A topological space X is *locally compact* iff each point in X has at least one neighborhood whose closure is compact.

Miscellaneous Exercises 7.3

1. (a) See the following results in Ch 3: 1.12 and 1 and 2 in 1.6. Then conclude that a polynomial function f: $R \longrightarrow R$ [i.e., for each x in R, $f(x) = ax^n + bx^{n-1} + \ldots + k$, where $a, b, \ldots, k$ are fixed elements of R and n is a fixed element of N] is continuous.

   (b) Prove: If the n in (a) is odd, then there is at least one r in R such that $f(r) = 0$.

   (c) Let g: $R \longrightarrow R$ be given by: For each x in R, $g(x) = |x|$. Prove g is continuous.

   (d) Let T be the open interval in R from -1 to 1, and let h: $T \longrightarrow R$ be given by: For each x in T, $h(x) = 1 - |x|$. Observe that h is continuous.

   (e) Let j: $T \longrightarrow R$ be given by: For each x in T, $j(x) = 1/(1 - |x|)$. Prove j is continuous. [See 2 in 3.3 and 5(b) in 1.6 of Ch 3.]

   (f) Let m: $T \longrightarrow R$ be given by: For each x in T, $m(x) = x/(1 - |x|)$. Prove m is a homeomorphism of T onto R.

   (g) Prove: If (a, b) and (c, d) are open intervals in R, then (a, b) and (c, d) are homeomorphic. [Hence each open interval in R is homeomorphic to R.]

   (h) Is there a closed interval in R which is homeomorphic to R?

2. Prove:

   (a) Complete normality is hereditary.

   (b) A space X is completely normal iff each subspace of X is normal.

   [The only if part follows trivially from (a) and 5.4.]

3. Prove:

   (a) Regularity is hereditary.

   (b) Each second countable regular space is completely normal.

   [Use 2(b) and 6.7.]

4. Show that each space in 5.7 is first countable and separable but not second countable.

5. Let f be a continuous map of a countably compact T_1 space X into a space Y. Prove $f[X]$ is countably compact. (1.1 and 1.3.) [Compare this result with 4 and 5 in 4.9 of Ch 3 and 3.4 of Ch 3.]

6.   Let X, Y, $\mathcal{T}$, and $\mathcal{F}$ be as given in 7.1.   Prove:

   (a) $\mathcal{F}$ is a topology for Y.

   (b) Y is $\mathcal{F}$-compact.

   (c) $(X, \mathcal{T})$ is a subspace of $(Y, \mathcal{F})$.

7.   Prove that the space Y in 7.1 is T_2 iff X is locally compact and T_2.

8.   If A is an uncountable subset of a second countable space, then some point of A is a limit point of A.

9.   (a) Prove: If X is a separable space, then each family of disjoint open subsets of X is countable.

   (b) Prove: If X is a second countable space, then each family of disjoint open subsets of X is countable.

   (c) Give an example to show that the converse of (a) is not true.

10.   (a) Give an example of a compact set whose closure is not compact.

   (b) Prove: If A is a compact subset of a regular space, then A^- is compact.

5

Product Spaces

1. The Product of Two Spaces

Theorem 1.1. Let $(X, \mathcal{T})$ and $(Y, \mathcal{F})$ be topological spaces, and let $\mathcal{B} = \{U \times V : U \in \mathcal{T} \text{ and } V \in \mathcal{F}\}$. Then $\mathcal{B}$ is a base for a topology for $X \times Y$. [Use 3.5 in Ch 2.]

Definition 1.2. The topology $\mathcal{U}$ generated by $\mathcal{B}$ in 1.1 is called the *product topology* for $X \times Y$, and $(X \times Y, \mathcal{U})$ is the *product space* (of X and Y).

Exercises 1.3

Let $(X, \mathcal{T})$, $(Y, \mathcal{F})$, $\mathcal{B}$ and $\mathcal{U}$ be the same as in 1.1 and 1.2.

1. Prove: If $\mathcal{C}$ is a base for $\mathcal{T}$ and $\mathcal{D}$ is a base for $\mathcal{F}$, then $\{U \times V : U \in \mathcal{C} \text{ and } V \in \mathcal{D}\}$ is a base for the product topology $\mathcal{U}$. [3.3 in Ch 2.]

95

2.   Prove: In case $X = R = Y$ and both $\mathscr{T}$ and $\mathscr{F}$ are the usual topology for R, then $\mathcal{U}$ is the usual topology for E_2. [By 1, the family of all "open rectangles" is a base for $\mathcal{U}$. We observed earlier that the family of all spheres is a base for the usual topology for E_2. Use 3.3 in Ch 2.]

3.   [By 2, E_2 (with the usual topology) is the product space of R and R.]

(a) Give an example of an open subset G of the product space E_2 such that G is not of the form $U \times V$, where U and V are open subsets of R.

(b) Give an example of a subset H of E_2 such that H is not the Cartesian product of subsets of R.

4.   Prove: If X and Y are second countable spaces, then the product space $X \times Y$ is second countable.   [Use 1.]

5.   Prove: If X and Y are separable, then the product space is separable.

Remark 1.4.   Let $X \times Y$ be a product space, and let $f \colon X \times Y \longrightarrow X$ be the map defined by $f((x, y)) = x$ for each (x, y) in $X \times Y$.

(a) The map f is continuous.

(b) Let c be a fixed point in Y, and let $A = X \times \{c\}$.   The restriction of f to A is a homeomorphism of the subspace A onto X.

(c) Similarly, the map g defined by $g((x, y)) = y$ is continuous, and Y is homeomorphic to each subspace of $X \times Y$ of the form $\{x\} \times Y$, where $x \in X$.

Proof. (after giving your proof) (a) Let U be an open subset of X. Then $f^{-1}[U] = U \times Y$, which (by 1.2) is a base member of the product topology (since Y is open in Y).   Therefore, by 1.4[(d)] in Ch 3, f is continuous.   [By a base member of the product topology, we mean a member of the base given in 1.1.]

(b) Now f_A is a one-to-one continuous map of A onto X [2.2(c) in Ch 3]. To show f_A is open, first let $B = A \cap (W \times V)$, where $W \times V$ is a base member of the product topology and $c \in V$.   Then $f_A[B] = W$, which is open in X.   But any set open in A is a union of sets of the form of B; and since

$$f_A[\bigcup \mathcal{C}] = \bigcup \{f_A[B] \colon \quad B \in \mathcal{C}\}$$

for any collection of subsets of A, it follows that f_A is an open map, and hence a homeomorphism (4.4 in Ch 3).

Theorem I.5.   A non-void product space $X \times Y$ is connected iff X is connected and Y is connected.

Proof of the if part.   (The other part is yours.) Suppose X is connected and Y is connected.   So suppose c is a fixed point in Y.   Then (in view of 3.1 in Ch 3) 1.4(b) gives the result that the subspace $A = X \times \{c\}$ is connected.   Hence (by the last sentence before 5.9 in Ch 2) A is a connected subset of $X \times Y$.   Similarly, for each x in X, the set $H(x) = \{x\} \times Y$ is connected.   Now for any one x in X, $(x, c) \in H(x) \cap A$.   (See the diagram.)

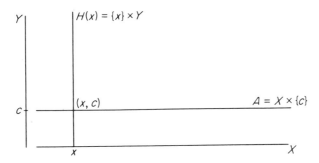

Hence, by 1 in 5.8 of Ch 2, $K(x) = H(x) \cup A$ is connected for each x in X. Now $A \subset K(x)$ for each x in X, and so no two members of $\{K(x): \ x \in X\}$ are separated.   Again by 1 in 5.8 of Ch 2, $\bigcup\{K(x): \ x \in X\}$ is connected. But this union is $X \times Y$.

Corollary I.6.   The space E_2 is connected.

Definition I.7.   Let X be a set.   Then $\{(x, x): \ x \in X\}$ is called the *diagonal* in $X \times X$ and is often denoted by Δ.

Exercises I.8

1. Prove: If X and Y are T_2 spaces, then the product space $X \times Y$ is T_2.

2. Prove: A space X is T_2 iff the diagonal Δ is a closed subset of the product space $X \times X$ (i.e., iff $X \times X \sim \Delta$ is open).

2. The Product of n Spaces

Suppose, for each i in N_n, X_i is a set (where n is a fixed integer greater than 2).   We must first agree upon what we shall mean by the "Cartesian product of these sets". We might be tempted to say hastily that the product set is the set of all "ordered n-tuples" $(x_1, x_2, \ldots, x_n)$, where $x_i \in X_i$ for each i in N_n. But this is vague and nonmathematical (since we have not defined "ordered n-tuple" of this kind). We are led by this intuitive idea, however, to lay down the following precise definition.

Definition 2.1.   For each i in N_n (where n is a fixed integer greater than 2), let X_i be a set. The set of all mappings x of N_n into $\bigcup\{X_i: \ i \in N_n\}$, such that $x(i) \in X_i$ for each i in N_n, is called the *Cartesian product* of the given sets and is denoted by $\times \{X_i: \ i \in N_n\}$ or by $X_1 \times \ldots \times X_n$.

Of course, for a given x in $\times \{X_i: \ i \in N_n\}$, we often use x_i to denote $x(i)$ and we use $(x_1, x_2, \ldots, x_n)$ to denote x itself. Also, x_i is called the *ith coordinate of x*.

[According to our intuitive idea, a fixed "n-tuple" $(x_1, x_2, \ldots, x_n)$ is "something" which assigns to each i in N_n an element x_i in X_i (so that $x_i \in \bigcup\{X_i: \ i \in N_n\}$). Such a "something" is a map (say x) of N_n into $\bigcup\{X_i: \ i \in N_n\}$. So we call it a map. It is just as easy to interpret 2.1 as to interpret the vague reference to ordered n-tuples. We shall also see that 2.1 generalizes easily when we are ready to define the Cartesian product of an arbitrary collection of sets.]

Exercises 2.2

Let $n \in N$ with $n \geq 2$. For each i in N_n, let X_i be a set. Let $X = X_1 \times \ldots \times X_n$. (In case $n = 2$, X is defined from Ch 1.) For each i in N_n, let $A_i \subset X_i$ and $B_i \subset X_i$.

1. Prove: If, for each i in N_n, $A_i \subset B_i$, then

$$A_1 \times \ldots \times A_n \subset B_1 \times \ldots \times B_n.$$

[Observe that $x \in A_1 \times \ldots \times A_n$ iff $x_i \in A_i$ for each i in N_n.]

2. Give an example to show that

$$(A_1 \times \ldots \times A_n) \cup (B_1 \times \ldots \times B_n)$$

need not equal $(A_1 \cup B_1) \times \ldots \times (A_n \cup B_n)$. [Take $n = 2$ and $X_1 = X_2 = R$.]

3. Prove:

$(A_1 \times \ldots \times A_n) \cap (B_1 \times \ldots \times B_n) = (A_1 \cap B_1) \times \ldots \times (A_n \cap B_n)$.
[Just notice that x belongs to either side of this equality iff x_i belongs to A_i and to B_i for each i in N_n.]

Definition 2.3.   Let $n \in N$ such that $n \geq 2$, for each i in N_n let X_i be a set, and let $X = X_1 \times \ldots \times X_n$.

(a) The set X_i is called the *ith coordinate set* (*of X*).

(b) For a given i in N_n, let f_i be the map of X into X_i defined by $f_i(x) = x_i$ for each x in X.   The map f_i is called the *ith projection mapping* or the *ith projection.*

Remark 2.4.   Let $A_i \subset X_i$ in 2.3 for each i in N_n.

(a) For a fixed i, an element x in X belongs to $f_i^{-1}[A_i]$ iff the ith coordinate x_i of x belongs to A_i, where f_i is (as usual) the ith projection.

(b) For a fixed i,

$$f_i^{-1}[A_i] = X_1 \times X_2 \times \ldots A_i \times \ldots \times X_n.$$

(c) $f_1^{-1}[A_1] \cap \ldots \cap f_n^{-1}[A_n] = A_1 \times A_2 \times \ldots \times A_n.$

Concerning (b), we merely say that an element x of the product set X belongs to $f_i^{-1}[A_i]$ iff $x_i \in A_i$, and this same criterion determines whether or not $x \in X_1 \times X_2 \times \ldots \times A_i \times \ldots \times X_n$.

An x in X belongs to the set on the left in (c) iff $x_i \in A_i$ for each i in N_n; the same criterion determines whether or not x belongs to the set on the right.   So the equality holds.

Theorem 2.5.   Let $n \in N$ with $n \geq 2$, and for each i in N_n let $(X_i, \mathcal{T}_i)$ be a topological space.   Then the family

$$\mathcal{B} = \{U_1 \times \ldots \times U_n : \quad U_i \in \mathcal{T}_i \quad \text{for each } i \text{ in } N_n\}$$

is a base for a topology for $X_1 \times \ldots \times X_n$.

Proof. Since X_i is open, $X_1 \times \ldots \times X_n \in \mathcal{B}$;   so (a) in 3.5 of Ch 2 holds.   To see that (b) holds, observe that if $U, V \in \mathcal{B}$, then $U \cap V \in \mathcal{B}$. [For $U = U_1 \times \ldots \times U_n$ and $V = V_1 \times \ldots \times V_n$ where U_i, V_i are open in X_i.   By 3 in 2.2,

$$U \cap V = (U_1 \cap V_1) \times \ldots \times (U_n \cap V_n) \subset \mathcal{B}$$

since $U_i \cap V_i$ is open in X_i.]   Thus $\mathcal{B}$ is a base for a topology for $X_1 \times \ldots \times X_n$ by 3.5 in Ch 2.

Definition 2.6.   The topology $\mathcal{U}$ generated by $\mathcal{B}$ in 2.5 is called the *product topology* for the set $X_1 \times \ldots \times X_n$, and $(X_1 \times \ldots \times X_n, \mathcal{U})$ is called the *product space* (of the given spaces).

Remark 2.7.   Each of the projection maps f_i of the product space in 2.5 is a continuous map into X_i.

Proof. For a fixed i in N_n, let U_i be an open subset of X_i. Then [by 2.4(b)]

$$f_i^{-1}[U_i] = X_1 \times X_2 \times \ldots U_i \times \ldots \times X_n$$

which belongs to the $\mathscr{B}$ in 2.5. So $f_i^{-1}[U_i]$ is open, and (by 1.4[(d) $\longrightarrow$ (a)] in Ch 3) f_i is continuous.

Remark 2.8.   The product topology $\mathfrak{U}$ is the smallest topology for the set $X_1 \times \ldots \times X_n$ in 2.6 for which each projection map f_i is a continuous map into the space $(X_i, \mathscr{T}_i)$.

Proof. [By 2.7 each map f_i is continuous relative to $\mathfrak{U}$. So it only remains to show that $\mathfrak{U} \subset \mathscr{T}$ if $\mathscr{T}$ is a topology which makes each f_i continuous.] Suppose $\mathscr{T}$ is a topology for $X_1 \times \ldots \times X_n$ such that f_i is continuous relative to $\mathscr{T}$ and $\mathscr{T}_i$ for each i in N_n. Let $B \in \mathscr{B}$ where $\mathscr{B}$ is the base in 2.5 and 2.6. Then

$$B = U_1 \times \ldots \times U_n,$$

where $U_i \in \mathscr{T}_i$ for each i in N_n. Since f_i is $\mathscr{T}_i - \mathscr{T}$-continuous, it follows that $f_i^{-1}[U_i] \in \mathscr{T}$ (by 1.4[(a) $\longrightarrow$ (d)] in Ch 3) for each i in N_n. Hence

$$f_1^{-1}[U_1] \cap \ldots \cap f_n^{-1}[U_n] \in \mathscr{T}.$$

But, by 2.4(c),

$$f_1^{-1}[U_1] \cap \ldots \cap f_n^{-1}[U_n] = U_1 \times \ldots \times U_n = B,$$

and $B \in \mathscr{T}$. So $\mathscr{B} \subset \mathscr{T}$. Hence $\mathfrak{U} \subset \mathscr{T}$ and 2.8 is proved.

Since the product topology $\mathfrak{U}$ in 2.6 is the smallest topology for the set $\times \{X_i : i \in N_n\}$ which makes all the projections continuous, a review of the answer to 9 in 1.6 of Ch 3 (including 1.7 in Ch 3) shows that a subbase for $\mathfrak{U}$ is the family $\mathcal{S}$ of all sets of the form $f_i^{-1}[U_i]$, where $U_i \in \mathscr{T}_i$ and $i \in N_n$. Thus, for the set $X_1 \times \ldots \times X_n$ in 2.5, the following three topologies are identical:

1. the product topology $\mathfrak{U}$ defined in 2.6,
2. the smallest topology for $X_1 \times \ldots \times X_n$ which makes all the projection maps continuous,
3. the topology which has the family $\mathcal{S} = \{f_i^{-1}[U_i] : U_i \in \mathscr{T}_i \text{ and } i \in N_n\}$ as a subbase.

So, for a finite family of spaces, we could have defined the product topology by any one of the three descriptions 1, 2, or 3.

Exercises 2.9

1. Suppose $\mathcal{B}_i$ is a base for $\mathcal{T}_i$ in 2.5, and let

$$\mathcal{C} = \{B_1 \times \ldots \times B_n : \quad B_i \in \mathcal{B}_i \text{ for each } i \text{ in } N_n\}.$$

Prove: $\mathcal{C}$ is a base for the product topology for $\times \{X_i : \quad i \in N_n\}$.

2. Prove: If in 2.5 each $X_i = R$ and each $\mathcal{T}_i$ is the usual topology for R, then the product space $(R \times R \times \ldots \times R, \mathcal{U})$ in 2.6 is the topological space $(E_n, \mathcal{T})$, where $\mathcal{T}$ is the metric topology induced by the usual metric for E_n given in 7.9 of Ch 2.   [Use 1 above and 3.3 in Ch 2.   The family $\mathcal{D}$ of all spheres is a base for $\mathcal{T}$.   The base $\mathcal{C}$ in 1 for $\mathcal{U}$ will be the family of "n-dimensional cubes" if each base $\mathcal{B}_i$ in 1 is taken to be the family of open intervals in R.]

3. General Product Spaces

Since product spaces are extremely important, we wish to define what we mean by the product of an arbitrary collection of topological spaces.

The answers to 9 in 1.6 of Ch 3 and 1.7 and 1.8 of Ch 3 were provided for our convenience here.   So it is in order to turn back and review that discussion before becoming involved in this section.

It is very simple to generalize Definition 2.1 to the notion of the Cartesian product of an arbitrary collection of sets.   The set N_n in 2.1 is just an index set—which happens to be finite.   Here, we simply replace the finite index set N_n by an arbitrary index set, say A.   Except for this replacement, our first definition here [3.1(a)] reads exactly as 2.1.

Definition 3.1.   For each a in an index set A, let X_a be a set.

(a) The set $\{x : \quad x \text{ is a map of } A \text{ into } \bigcup \{X_a : \quad a \in A\} \text{ such that } x(a) \in X_a$ for each a in $A\}$ is called the *Cartesian product* of the indexed collection $\{X_a : \quad a \in A\}$ and is denoted by $\times \{X_a : \quad a \in A\}$.

(b) Let $a \in A$.   The set X_a is called the *ath coordinate set* of the product. If $x \in \times \{X_a : \quad a \in A\}$, then $x(a)$ is called the *ath coordinate* of x and is often denoted by x_a.

(c) Let $a \in A$.   The map f_a of $\times \{X_a : \quad a \in A\}$ into X_a defined by $f_a(x) = x_a$ for each x in $\times \{X_a : \quad a \in A\}$ is called the *ath projection (mapping)*.

Exercises 3.2

Let $X = \times \{X_a: \ a \in A\}$, where A and X_a are the same as in 3.1.

1. Let $b \in A$ and let $U \subset X_b$. Describe the set $f_b^{-1}[U]$ in words. [In discussing product spaces, if b is an element of the index set A, then f_b denotes the bth projection map.]

2. Let $F \subset A$, and for each a in F let $U_a \subset X_a$.

   (a) Fill in the following blank to make a correct statement:

   $$\bigcap \{f_a^{-1}[U_a]: \ a \in F\} = \{x: \ x \in X \text{ and } \underline{\hspace{3cm}}\}.$$

   (b) Show that

   $$\bigcap \{f_a^{-1}[U_a]: \ a \in F\} = \times \{V_a: \ a \in A\},$$

   where $V_a = X_a$ if $a \in A \sim F$ while, for a in F, $V_a = U_a$.

Answer to 1. $f_b^{-1}[U]$ is the set of all x in X whose bth coordinates are elements of U. [Or $f_b^{-1}[U]$ is the set of all members of X whose bth co-ordinates are restricted to lie in U while all other coordinates are unrestricted in the respective coordinate sets. In symbols, $f_b^{-1}[U] = \{x: \ x \in X \text{ and } x_b \in U\}$.]

Of course the set $\bigcap \{f_a^{-1}[U_a]: \ a \in F\}$ in 2 is

$$\{x: \ x \in X \text{ and } x_a \in U_a \text{ for each } a \text{ in } F\}.$$

Now suppose that for each a in an index set A, $(X_a, \mathcal{T}_a)$ is a topological space. The question arises: What topology should we adopt and call the product topology for the set $\times \{X_a: \ a \in A\}$? It turns out that the smallest topology for $\times \{X_a: \ a \in A\}$ which makes all the projection mappings continuous is a most useful one to the mathematical analyst. Further, we see from the concluding remarks of section 2 (just before 2.9) that what we "naturally" called the product topology in that finite case could have been equivalently defined as the smallest topology which makes all pro-jections continuous. So the smallest topology for $\times \{X_a: \ a \in A\}$ which makes all the projections continuous is the one which we shall call the product topology—although we shall describe it by a different, but equivalent, criterion in our formal definition to follow. We know that if each of the projections is to be continuous then for each a in A and each open set U_a in X_a, the set $f_a^{-1}[U_a]$ must be open and that (by 1.7 in Ch 3) the smallest topology for which this is so, is the one which has as subbase the family $\mathcal{S} = \{f_a^{-1}[U_a]: a \in A \text{ and } U_a \in \mathcal{T}_a\}$.

Definition 3.3.   For each a in an index set A, let $(X_a, \mathscr{T}_a)$ be a topological space, and let $X = \times \{X_a: \ a \in A\}$. The topology $\mathscr{T}$ for X which has as a subbase the family

$$\mathcal{S} = \{f_a^{-1}[U_a]: \ a \in A \text{ and } U_a \in \mathscr{T}_a \}$$

is called the *product topology* (or the *Tychonoff topology*) for X. The space $(X, \mathscr{T})$ is called the *product space* (of the given spaces).

Remark 1.8 in Ch 3 gives:

Remark 3.4.   Let $\mathscr{B}$ be the family of subsets of the set X in 3.3 defined so that a subset B of X belongs to $\mathscr{B}$ iff

$$B = \bigcap \{f_a^{-1}[U_a]: \ a \in F\}$$

for some finite subset F of A and some U_a in $\mathscr{T}_a$ for each a in F. Then $\mathscr{B}$ is a base for the product topology in 3.3.

Throughout this chapter when we refer to a subbase member of a product topology, we mean a member of the defining subbase $\mathcal{S}$ in 3.3; and when we refer to a base member, we mean a member of the base in 3.4. We see from 2(b) in 3.2 that a base member is a set of the form $\times \{U_a: \ a \in A\}$, where, for each a in A, $U_a \in \mathscr{T}_a$ and, for all but a finite number of a's, $U_a = X_a$.

So each open set in the product space X of 3.3 must contain a set (a base member) of the form $\times \{U_a: \ a \in A\}$, where $U_a = X_a$ for all but a finite number of a's in A. (Hence if G is non-empty and open in X of 3.3, then all but a finite number of coordinates of points in G are unrestricted in the respective coordinate spaces.) Thus if A is infinite, then a set H of the form $\times \{U_a: \ a \in A\}$ definitely is not open in the product space (as defined in 3.3) if U_a is an open proper subset of X_a for each a in A (for all coordinates of points in H are restricted to lie in the respective U_a's). [We do not call $\varnothing$ a proper subset.] It is true that the family $\mathcal{C}$ of all sets of the form $\times \{U_a: \ a \in A\}$, where $U_a \in \mathscr{T}_a$ for each a in A, is a base for some topology $\mathcal{F}$ for the product set $\times \{X_a: \ a \in A\}$; but (as just observed) this topology $\mathcal{F}$ is not, in general, the same as the topology $\mathscr{T}$ in 3.3, which we have chosen to call the product topology. Actually, in view of 2.6, this last mentioned topology $\mathcal{F}$ would have been a possible candidate to call the product topology. But this topology does not yield the desired theorems and results and is not as useful to the mathematician as the topology in 3.3. So we do not study the topology $\mathcal{F}$ here. This topology $\mathcal{F}$ is sometimes called the *box topology* for $\times \{X_a: \ a \in A\}$. Let us state formally two of the conclusions in the present discussion. Remark α follows from the last sentence of the preceding paragraph.

Remark α.   If B is a non-void member of the base $\mathcal{B}$ in 3.4, then $f_a[B] = X_a$ for all but a finite number of a's.

Since each non-void open set contains a non-void base member, we also have:

Remark β.   If G is a non-void open subset of the product space X in 3.3, then $f_a[G] = X_a$ for all but a finite number of a's.

Theorem 3.5.   If each space X_a in 3.3 is T_2, then the product space X is T_2.

Proof.   Suppose $x, y \in X$ with $x \neq y$. Then $x_b \neq y_b$ for some b in A. Since X_b is T_2, there are disjoint open sets U and V in X_b with $x_b \in U$ and $y_b \in V$. So $f_b^{-1}[U]$ and $f_b^{-1}[V]$ are disjoint neighborhoods of x and y respectively.

Theorem 3.6.   If X in 3.3 is T_2, then each coordinate space X_a is T_2 [provided no X_a is null].

Proof.   Contrapositively, suppose there is a coordinate space, say X_b, which is not T_2. Then there must be two distinct points, say s and t, in X_b which do not have disjoint neighborhoods. [Since no X_a is null, we can now build two distinct points x and y in X which do not have disjoint neighborhoods.]   For each a in $A \sim \{b\}$, let x_a be some point in X_a, and let $x_b = s$. Let x be the point in X such that $x(a)$ is the x_a just selected for each a in A. Let y be the element in X such that $y_a = x_a$ if $a \in A \sim \{b\}$ while $y_b = t$.

Now let U and V be any neighborhoods of x and y respectively. Then $U \supset \times \{U_a: \quad a \in A\}$ for some U_a in $\mathcal{T}_a$ with $x_a \in U_a$ (since U must contain a base member containing x). [Yes, $U_a = X_a$ for all but a finite number of a's, but this is immaterial here.]   Also $V \supset \times \{V_a: \quad a \in A\}$, where $y_a \in V_a \in \mathcal{T}_a$ for each a in A. Since $x_b = s$ and $y_b = t$, there must be a point p in $U_b \cap V_b$. Let z be the element of X such that $z_a = x_a = y_a$ if $a \in A \sim \{b\}$ while $z_b = p$. Then $z \in U \cap V$, and X is not T_2.

As we would hope, a map g of a space Z into a product space is continuous iff g is "coordinatewise continuous" in the sense that $f_a \circ g$ is continuous for each projection f_a. Also a sequence S in a product space converges to a point x iff $f_a \circ S$ converges to x_a for each a in the index set.

Theorem 3.7.   Let g be a map of a space Z into the product space X of 3.3.   Then g is continuous iff $f_a \circ g$ is continuous for each a in A.

Proof. Since f_a is continuous, the only if part follows from the fact that the composition of continuous maps is continuous [5(b) in 1.6 of Ch 3].

[We use 1.5 in Ch 3 to prove the if part.] Suppose $f_a \circ g$ is continuous for each a in A, and let W be any member of the subbase $\mathcal{S}$ in 3.3. Then $W = f_b^{-1}[U]$ for some b in A and some U in $\mathcal{T}_b$. Now

$$g^{-1}[W] = g^{-1}[f_b^{-1}[U]] = (f_b \circ g)^{-1}[U]$$

by 5(a) in 1.6 of Ch 3. But (since $f_b \circ g$ is continuous) $(f_b \circ g)^{-1}[U]$ must be open in Z by 1.4(d) in Ch 3. Hence $g^{-1}[W]$ is open in Z and g is continuous by 1.5 in Ch 3.

Remark 3.8. Let $\mathcal{S}$ be a subbase for a topology for a space Z, let S be a sequence in Z, and let $x \in Z$. If S is eventually in each member of $\mathcal{S}$ containing x, then S converges to x.

Proof. Let U be any neighborhood of x. Then U contains a base neighborhood $V_1 \cap V_2 \cap \ldots \cap V_k$ of x, where $V_i \in \mathcal{S}$ for each i in N_k. By hypothesis, for each i in N_k there is an integer m_i such that $S(n) \in V_i$ for $n \geq m_i$. Let

$$m = \max \{m_1, m_2, \ldots, m_k\}.$$

Now if $n \geq m$,

$$S(n) \in V_1 \cap V_2 \cap \ldots \cap V_k \subset U.$$

Hence S converges to x.

Theorem 3.9. Let S be a sequence in the product space X of 3.3. Then S converges to a point x in X iff $f_a \circ S$ converges to x_a for each a in A.

Proof. The only if part follows from 1.9 in Ch 3. So suppose $f_a \circ S$ converges to x_a for each a in A, and let $f_b^{-1}[U]$ be any member of the subbase $\mathcal{S}$ in 3.3 such that $x \in f_b^{-1}[U]$, where $U \in \mathcal{T}_b$. Then $x_b \in U$ and by hypothesis $f_b \circ S$ converges to x_b. So there is an m in N such that

$$(f_b \circ S)(n) = f_b(S(n)) \in U, \quad \text{i.e.,} \quad S(n) \in f_b^{-1}[U]$$

for each $n \geq m$ in N. So S is eventually in $f_b^{-1}[U]$, an arbitrary member of $\mathcal{S}$ containing x. Hence, by 3.8, S converges to x.

Theorem 3.10. Each projection map f_a of the product space X in 3.3 is an open map.

Proof. Suppose $b \in A$, and let W be a base member of the product topology (i.e., $W \in \mathcal{B}$ in 3.4). By the first paragraph after 3.4, there is a finite subset F of A such that $W = \times \{U_a : a \in A\}$, where for each a in A, $U_a \in \mathcal{T}_a$ and $U_a = X_a$ if $a \in A \sim F$. So $f_b[W] = U_b$, which is open in X_b. Now let V be any open subset of X. Then V is the union of a family $\mathcal{C}$ of base members of the form W. So

$$f_b[V] = f_b[\bigcup \mathcal{C}] = \bigcup \{f_b[C] : C \in \mathcal{C}\}$$

by 1(a) in 3.10 of Ch 1. We have just shown that $f_b[C]$ is open for each base member C in $\mathcal{C}$. Hence $f_b[V]$ is open.

It is natural to ask if projections are closed maps. To answer this question, consider the space $E_2 = R \times R$. Let $H = \{(x, y): x, y \in R$ and $xy = 2\}$. Observe that H is closed in E_2, but $f_1[H] = R \sim \{0\}$ which is not closed (where f_1 is the projection into the "first coordinate space" R).

Theorem 3.10 may be used to prove our next theorem. I leave the proof for your pleasure (although it is hard to resist the temptation of giving my proof).

Theorem 3.11.   If the product space X in 3.3 is first countable, then each of the coordinate spaces is first countable (provided $X \neq \varnothing$).

We have the stronger theorem:

Theorem 3.12.   The product space X in 3.3 is first countable iff each of the coordinate spaces is first countable and all but a countable number of the coordinate spaces are indiscrete (provided $X \neq \varnothing$).

Proof. First, suppose that for each a in A, X_a is first countable and that all but a countable number of the spaces X_a are indiscrete. Let $B = \{a: a \in A$ and X_a is not indiscrete$\}$. Then B is countable. Let $x \in X$. For each a in A, let $\mathcal{C}_a$ be a countable local base at x_a in the space X_a. Then for each a in $A \sim B$, $\mathcal{C}_a = \{X_a\}$ since for such a, X_a is indiscrete.

For each fixed a in B, let $\mathcal{F}_a$ be the countable family $\{f_a^{-1}[U]: U \in \mathcal{C}_a\}$ for the fixed a. Let

$$\mathcal{F} = \{V: V \in \mathcal{F}_a \text{ for } a \in B\} = \bigcup\{\mathcal{F}_a: a \in B\}.$$

(Now $\mathcal{F}$ is a countable family, since it is the union of a countable collection of countable families.) So there are only a countable number of finite subfamilies of $\mathcal{F}$ [by (β) in our discussion of 4 in 3.9 of Ch 2]. Hence the family $\mathcal{D}$ of intersections of all finite subfamilies of $\mathcal{F}$ is a countable family. But, clearly, $\mathcal{D}$ is a local base at x. Therefore X is first countable.

To prove the converse, suppose X is first countable. By 3.11, each space X_a is first countable. Again, let

$$B = \{a: a \in A \text{ and } X_a \text{ is not indiscrete}\}.$$

Suppose B were uncountable. Now for each a in B, let U_a be an open proper subset of X_a, and let $z_a \in U_a$. Let y be some element of X such that $y_a = z_a$ for each a in B. Let $\mathcal{U}$ be a countable local base $\{W_1, W_2, W_3, \ldots\}$ at y.

By Remark β (just before 3.5), $f_a[W_1] = X_a$ except for a finite set F_1 of a's. Also, for each i in N, $f_a[W_i] = X_a$ except for a finite set F_i of a's.

Now $\bigcup\{F_i: \ i \in N\}$ is countable, and so, cannot contain the uncountable set B. This means there is some b in B such that, for each i in N, $b \notin F_i$, i.e., $f_b[W_i] = X_b$ for each i in N. But then $f_b^{-1}[U_b]$ is a neighborhood of y (since $y_b = z_b \in U_b$) which does not contain any W_i in $\mathfrak{U}$—contradicting the fact that $\mathfrak{U}$ is a local base at y. We must reject our supposition that B is uncountable.

The notion of a function of several variables and the notion of continuity in each variable are common in analysis. Let us consider the case of two variables and state our definition to be used in the exercises which follow. The case for more than two variables is similar.

Definition 3.13. Let f be a map of a product space $X \times Y$ into a space Z. [We denote the image of (x, y) by $f(x, y)$ and call f a function of two variables.] For each fixed y in Y, let $g_y: \ X \longrightarrow Z$ be the map defined by $g_y(x) = f(x, y)$ for each x in X. Also, for each fixed x in X, let h_x be defined by $h_x(y) = f(x, y)$ for each y in Y. Then f is said to be *continuous in x* iff for each fixed y in Y, g_y is a continuous map of X into Z. Similarly f is *continuous in y* iff h_x is continuous for each x in X.

Miscellaneous Exercises 3.14

1. Prove: The product of any collection of T_1 spaces is T_1. (Use 8 in 1.18 of Ch 2.)

2. Prove: The product of any collection of regular spaces is regular. [Use 5.9(a) in Ch 4.]

3. Let X be the space in 3 of 6.6 in Ch 2, and let Y be the product space $X \times X$. Show that Y is not a Lindelöf space. [*Hint:* Show that
$$A = \{(x, y): \ x + y = 0\}$$
is closed, and give an open cover for A which has no countable subcover. See 1 in 3.9 of Ch 2.] (So the product of Lindelöf spaces need not be a Lindelöf space.)

   [The space Y in 3 also shows that the product of normal spaces need not be normal. The space X in 3 is normal (see 3(b) in 6.8 of Ch 4). Let
$$B = \{(x, y): \ x + y = 0 \text{ and } x \text{ is rational}\}$$
and let
$$C = \{(x, y): \ x + y = 0 \text{ and } x \text{ is irrational}\}.$$

   It is easy to see that B and C are disjoint closed sets. There do not exist disjoint open sets about B and C, although this is not convenient to show at this stage. Is the space Y a T_3 space? (You may use 2 above.) So Y is another T_3 space which is not T_4.]

4. Let f be a map of a product space $X \times Y$ into a space Z.

(a) Prove: If f is a continuous map of $X \times Y$ into Z, then f is continuous in x and f is continuous in y (see 3.13).

(b) Show that the converse of (a) is not true. [Consider the map $f\colon E_2 \longrightarrow R$ defined by

$$f(x, y) = \frac{xy}{x^2 + y^2}$$

if $(x, y) \neq (0, 0)$ while $f(0, 0) = 0$.]

5. Let f be a map of a space X into a space Y. Let h be the map of X into $X \times Y$ defined by $h(x) = (x, f(x))$ for each x in X. Prove: If f is continuous, then h is continuous relative to the product topology for $X \times Y$. [Use 3.7.]

6. Let f be the map of the closed unit interval Q into R defined by $f(x) = \sin(\pi/x)$ if $0 < x \leq 1$ while $f(0) = 0$. [Let us accept here that "$\sin z$ is a continuous function of z". (This should be shown somewhere in your work in real analysis.) We know from our work (see 2 in 3.3 of Ch 4) that π/x is continuous on the subspace H of Q, where $H = \{x\colon 0 < x \leq 1\}$. So, by 5(b) in 1.6 of Ch 3, our given function f is continuous on H. Recall that f_H denotes the restriction of f to H.]

(a) Let $B = \{(x, f_H(x))\colon x \in H\}$. Prove that B is a connected subset of $H \times R$ (and hence is a connected subset of $R \times R$ or E_2). [Use 5 above, 6.5 in Ch 2, and 3.1 in Ch 3—3.1 being applied to the map described by h in 5.]

(b) Let $D = \{(0, y)\colon -1 \leq y \leq 1\}$ and let $E = B \cup D$. Prove E is a connected subset of E_2. [See 5.6 in Ch 2.]

(c) Let $F = \{(x, f(x))\colon x \in Q\}$. Prove F is connected in E_2. [See 5.5 in Ch 2.]

(d) Prove F is not locally connected. [$(0, 0)$ is the point you want to consider.]

(e) Similarly E is not locally connected.

7. If you do not like to appeal to analysis for the continuity of the sine function, you may replace the function f in 6 by the function g described here. Let g be the map of Q into R whose "graph" in E_2

consists of $(0, 0)$ and the straight line segments joining the points $(1, 0)$, $(\frac{1}{2}, \frac{1}{4})$, $(\frac{1}{4}, 0)$, $(\frac{1}{8}, \frac{1}{4})$, . . . , $(\frac{1}{2^n}, y_n)$, . . . , where $y_n = 0$ if n is even and $y_n = \frac{1}{4}$ if n is odd.   See the figure.

We know that a linear function on R to R is continuous.   [See the following results in Ch 3:   1 and 4 in 1.6 and 1.12.]   So the map g defined above is continuous at each point of Q except 0.   Show that "the graph of g" (or g itself according to our definition of a

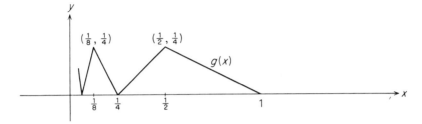

mapping in Ch 1) is a connected subset of E_2, but g is not locally connected.

8.   For each a in an index set A, let $(X_a, \mathcal{T}_a)$ be a topological space. Let $\mathcal{B}$ be the family of all sets of the form $\times \{U_a:\ a \in A\}$, where $U_a \in \mathcal{T}_a$.

(a) Prove $\mathcal{B}$ is a base for some topology for the set $\times \{X_a:\ a \in A\}$. The topology which has $\mathcal{B}$ as a base is sometimes called the *box topology*.

(b) Is the box topology for $\times \{X_a:\ a \in A\}$ larger than the product topology?

(c) Are the projections into the coordinate spaces continuous relative to the box topology?

6

Metric Spaces

1. Complete Normality of Metric Spaces

We know that a topological space is a generalization of a metric space. In this section, we shall show that a topological space which is restricted to be a T_5 space is still a generalization of a metric space. That is, we shall show that each metric space is completely normal (and hence T_5 since we observed earlier that metric spaces are T_2).

Definition 1.1. Let A, $B \subset X$, where (X, d) is a metric space. The *distance between A and B* is denoted by $d(A, B)$ and defined by

$$d(A, B) = 0 \quad \text{if} \quad A = \varnothing \quad \text{or} \quad B = \varnothing$$

$$d(A, B) = \inf \{d(x, y): \quad x \in A, y \in B\} \quad \text{if } A \neq \varnothing \quad \text{and} \quad B \neq \varnothing.$$

In case B is a singleton set $\{p\}$, we may write $d(A, p)$ for $d(A, \{p\})$.

Theorem 1.2. Let $A \subset X$, where (X, d) is a metric space. Let $f: X \longrightarrow R$ be defined by $f(x) = d(A, x)$ for each x in X. The map f is continuous.

Proof. Suppose $p \in X$ and let $\epsilon > 0$. For each x in A and a fixed q in X, we have

$$d(p, x) \leq d(p, q) + d(q, x).$$

From this we obtain (letting x range over A)

$$d(A, p) \leq d(p, q) + d(A, q),$$

i.e.,

(1) $$f(p) - f(q) \leq d(p, q).$$

Similarly

(2) $$f(q) - f(p) \leq d(p, q).$$

From (1) and (2), $|f(p) - f(q)| \leq d(p, q)$.   So, letting $\delta = \epsilon$, we have:

$$\text{if} \quad d(p, q) < \delta, \quad \text{then} \quad |f(p) - f(q)| < \epsilon.$$

Thus (1.3 in Ch 3) f is continuous at the arbitrary point p in X and hence is continuous.

Theorem I.3.   Let $A \subset X$, where (X, d) is a metric space and $A \neq \varnothing$. Then $A^- = \{x: \quad d(A, x) = 0\}$.

Proof.   Let f be the map defined in 1.2.   Then by 1.4(e) in Ch 3 and 1.2 above, $f^{-1}[\{0\}]$ is closed and surely contains A.   Hence

$$\{x: \quad d(A, x) = 0\} \supset A^-.$$

Now suppose $p \notin A^-$.   Then [7.7(b) in Ch 2] there is an $\epsilon > 0$ such that $A \cap S_\epsilon(p) = \varnothing$, i.e., $d(x, p) \geq \epsilon$ for each x in A and so $d(A, p) \geq \epsilon > 0$. Hence

$$\{x: \quad d(A, x) = 0\} \subset A^-.$$

We conclude that $A^- = \{x: \quad d(A, x) = 0\}$.

Theorem I.4.   Each metric space (X, d) is completely normal.

Proof.   Suppose A and B are separated subsets of X.   Let f be defined just as in 1.2, let $g: \quad X \longrightarrow R$ be defined by $g(x) = d(B, x)$ for x in X, and let h be defined by $h(x) = f(x) - g(x)$ for each x in X.   It follows from 4 and 5(b) in 1.6 of Ch 3, 1.12(a) of Ch 3, and 1.2 above that our present map h is continuous.   [Take $a = -1$ in 4, and write $f(x) - g(x)$ as $f(x) + -1g(x)$.]   Let

$$V = \{x: \quad d(A, x) - d(B, x) > 0\}.$$

Then $B \subset V$.   [For if $x_0 \in B$, then $d(B, x_0) = 0$ while (by 1.3) $d(A, x_0) > 0$ since $A^- \cap B = \varnothing$.]   But V is open since h is continuous and since $V = h^{-1}[W]$, where W is the open right ray

$$\{y: \quad y \in R \text{ and } y > 0\} \quad \text{in } R.$$

Similarly the set

$$U = \{x: \quad d(A, x) - d(B, x) < 0\}$$

is an open set containing A. Clearly $U \cap V = \varnothing$. Hence X is completely normal.

Corollary 1.5.   (a) Each metric space is T_5. (b) Each metric space is normal.

Exercises 1.6

1. Let A and B be non-void disjoint closed subsets of a metric space X with metric d. Prove:

    (a) If B is compact, then there is some point b in B such that $d(A, B) = d(A, b) > 0$.

    (b) If A and B are compact, then there are points a in A and b in B such that $d(A, B) = d(a, b)$.

    (c) The conclusion in (b) may not hold if A and B are not compact. Further, we may have $d(A, B) = 0$ if A and B are not compact (even though A and B are closed, disjoint and non-void). [Use a subspace of R for your example.]

2. Let (X, d) be a metric space. Prove that $d: \quad X \times X \longrightarrow R$ is continuous (where $X \times X$ has the product topology and each coordinate space X has the d-metric topology).

2. Products of Metric Spaces

Definition 2.1.   (a) Let $A \subset X$, where (X, d) is a metric space. The *diameter of A* is denoted by $d(A)$ and is defined by

$$d(A) = 0 \quad \text{if } A = \varnothing$$

$$d(A) = \sup \{d(x, y): \quad x, y \in A\} \quad \text{if } A \neq \varnothing,$$

where it is understood that sup $\{d(x, y): \quad x, y \in A\}$ is the element ∞ in the extended reals if the set $\{d(x, y): \quad x, y \in A\}$ is unbounded.

(b) The metric d is called a *bounded metric* for X iff $d(X)$ is a real number —not ∞.

Remark 2.2.   Let (X, d) be a metric space. The family of all r-spheres with $r < 1$ is a base for the d-metric topology.

Theorem 2.3. Let (X, d) be a metric space. There is a bounded metric e for X such that the e-metric topology is the same as the d-metric topology.

Proof. For each pair x, y in X, let $e(x, y) = \min \{1, d(x, y)\}$. It will be clear that e is a metric if we can prove the triangle inequality. To this end, suppose $x, y, z \in X$. We must show

(1) $$e(x, y) \leq e(x, z) + e(y, z).$$

If a term on the right is one, the inequality is clear. If neither term on the right is one, then

$$e(x, z) + e(y, z) = d(x, z) + d(y, z) \geq d(x, y) \geq e(x, y)$$

(since d is a metric), and (1) is proved. Now the family of r-spheres, with $r < 1$, is the same whether we use d or e as metric. So 2.2 shows that the e-metric topology is identical with the d-metric topology. Clearly e is a bounded metric—since $e(X) \leq 1$.

Theorem 2.4. For each n in N, let (X_n, d_n) be a metric space with $d_n(X_n) \leq 1$. For $x, y \in \times \{X_n : \ n \in N\}$, let

$$d(x, y) = \sum \{2^{-n} d_n(x_n, y_n) : \ n \in N\}$$

(where the notation denotes the sum of an infinite series). Then (a) d is a metric, and (b) $\mathcal{T} = \mathcal{F}$, where $\mathcal{T}$ is the d-metric topology and $\mathcal{F}$ the product topology for $\times \{X_n : \ n \in N\}$ (where X_n has the d_n-metric topology).

Proof. (a) That the series converges, follows from the fact that the nth term is non-negative and not greater than the nth term of the geometric series $\sum \{2^{-n} : \ n \in N\}$ (since $d_n(X_n) \leq 1$). To prove the triangle inequality, suppose $x, y, z \in \times \{X_n : \ n \in N\}$. Then (since each d_n is a metric)

$$\sum \{2^{-n} d_n(x_n, y_n) : \ n \in N_k\} \leq \sum \{2^{-n}[d_n(x_n, z_n) + d_n(z_n, y_n)] : \ n \in N_k\}$$
$$= \sum \{2^{-n} d_n(x_n, z_n) : \ n \in N_k\} + \sum \{2^{-n} d_n(z_n, y_n) : \ n \in N_k\}$$

for each k in N. "Taking the limit as k becomes large", we have

$$d(x, y) \leq d(x, z) + d(z, y).$$

(b) To prove $\mathcal{F} \subset \mathcal{T}$, let U be a subbase member of $\mathcal{F}$. Then

(1) $$U = \{x : \ x_k \in U_k\}$$

for some k in N and some open set U_k in X_k. Suppose $y \in U$. Then $y_k \in U_k$, and (since U_k is open in X_k) there is an $r > 0$ such that

(2) $$S_r(y_k) \subset U_k.$$

Let $W = S_t(y)$, where $t = 2^{-k}r$, and let $x \in W$. Then

$$2^{-k} d_k(x_k, y_k) \leq d(x, y) < 2^{-k}r$$

(the first inequality following from the definition of $d(x, y)$ in 2.4).   Hence $d_k(x_k, y_k) < r$, so that $x_k \in U_k$ by (2), and therefore $x \in U$ by (1).   Hence $W \subset U$ (since x is an arbitrary member of W).   This means that $U \in \mathcal{T}$. Now, since each subbase member of $\mathcal{F}$ belongs to $\mathcal{T}$, we have

(3) $\mathcal{F} \subset \mathcal{T}$.   (Why?)

To prove $\mathcal{T} \subset \mathcal{F}$, suppose $z \in G$ where $G \in \mathcal{T}$.   Then there is a q in N such that $S_{2^{-q}}(z) \subset G$.   Let

$$V = \{x: \quad d_n(x_n, z_n) < 2^{-q-n-2} \quad \text{for each } n \text{ in } N_{q+2}\}.$$

Then $V \subset G$.   For suppose $x \in V$.   Then

$$d(x, z) < \sum \{2^{-q-n-2}: \quad n \in N_{q+2}\} + \sum \{2^{-n}: \quad n = q+3, q+4, \ldots,\}$$
$$< 2^{-q-1} + 2^{-q-1} = 2^{-q}.$$

Hence $z \in V \subset S_{2^{-q}}(z) \subset G$.   But V is a base member of the product topology $\mathcal{F}$.   Therefore G is $\mathcal{F}$-open, i.e., $G \in \mathcal{F}$, and

(4) $\mathcal{T} \subset \mathcal{F}$.

Our theorem now follows from (3) and (4).

Exercises 2.5

1. Let $k \in N$, and for each n in N_k, let (X_n, d_n) be a metric space.   For each pair x, y in $\times \{X_n: \ n \in N_k\}$, let

    $$d(x, y) = \max \{d_n(x_n, y_n): \ n \in N_k\}.$$

    Prove that d is a metric and the d-metric topology is the product topology for $\times \{X_n: \ n \in N_k\}$.

2. Suppose that in 2.4 we had defined $d(x, y)$ to be

    $$\sup \{d_n(x_n, y_n): \ n \in N\}.$$

    Would the d-metric topology then be the product topology?   (*Hint:* A sphere with "small" radius (which is open relative to the d-metric topology) might restrict all coordinates of its points to proper subsets of the X_n spaces, and hence would not be open relative to the product topology; Remark β just before 3.5.)

Suppose that in 2.4 we had not assumed each metric d_n to be bounded.   In view of the proof of 2.3, there would be a metric e_n for X_n such that $e_n(X_n) \leq 1$ and e_n gives the same topology as d_n for X_n.   We could then apply 2.4 to the spaces (X_n, e_n) and conclude there is a metric for $\times \{X_n: \ n \in N\}$ which induces the product topology (even if the d_n's are not bounded). Hence.

Theorem 2.6.   For each n in N, let (X_n, d_n) be a metric space. Then there is a metric for $\times \{X_n: \ n \in N\}$ which induces the product topology.

Recall the following definition (given in the last paragraph of Ch 2):

Definition 2.7.   A topological space $(X, \mathcal{T})$ is *metrizable* iff there is a metric d *for* X such that the d-metric topology is the topology $\mathcal{T}$.

We may now combine 1 in 2.5 and 2.6 to obtain:

Theorem 2.8.   If $\{(X_a, \mathcal{T}_a): \ a \in A\}$ is a collection of metrizable spaces and A is countable, then the product space is metrizable.

Question 2.9.   Let $\{(X_a, \mathcal{T}_a): \ a \in A\}$ be a collection of metrizable spaces where A is uncountable. Is the product space metrizable? [Recall that each metric space is first countable and see 3.12 in Ch 5. If a space is not first countable, then it is not metrizable.]

3. Complete Metric Spaces

Definition 3.1.   Let (X, d) be a metric space. A sequence x in X is called a *Cauchy sequence* iff for each real number $\epsilon > 0$ there is an n in N such that $d(x_m, x_k) < \epsilon$ for each pair of integers $m, k > n$.

Definition 3.2.   A metric space (X, d) is said to be *complete* iff each Cauchy sequence in X converges to a point in X.

Exercises 3.3

1. Let x be a sequence in X, where (X, d) is a metric space. Prove: If x converges to a point p in X, then x is a Cauchy sequence.

2. Prove: Each compact metric space is complete.

3. Give an example of a metric space which is not complete.

4. Give an example of a complete metric space which is not compact.

5. Prove that R (with the usual metric) is complete. [Use 2 and the fact that the range of a Cauchy sequence in R is a subset of some closed interval.]

Definition 3.4.   Let x and y be Cauchy sequences in a metric space (X, d) and let S be the sequence in R such that $S_n = d(x_n, y_n)$ for each n in N. Then x and y are said to be *equivalent* iff S converges to 0.

Theorem 3.5.   Let x and y be sequences in a metric space (X, d) such that x converges to a point p in X.   Then y converges to p iff x and y are equivalent Cauchy sequences.

Proof. Suppose x and y are equivalent Cauchy sequences, and let $\epsilon > 0$. Since x converges to p, there is an n_0 in N such that $d(p, x_n) < \epsilon/2$ for $n > n_0$. Since x and y are equivalent, there is an n_1 in N such that $d(y_n, x_n) < \epsilon/2$ for $n > n_1$. Now if $n > \max \{n_0, n_1\}$,

$$d(p, y_n) \leq d(p, x_n) + d(x_n, y_n) < \frac{\epsilon}{2} + \frac{\epsilon}{2} = \epsilon.$$

Hence y converges to p.

Now suppose y converges to p. [We are given that x converges to p.] That x and y are Cauchy sequences follows from 1 in 3.3. Let $\epsilon > 0$. Since y converges to p, there is a k in N such that $d(p, y_n) < \epsilon/2$ for each $n > k$. Also there is an m in N such that $d(p, x_n) < \epsilon/2$ for $n > m$. For $n > \max \{k, m\}$,

$$d(x_n, y_n) \leq d(p, x_n) + d(p, y_n) < \frac{\epsilon}{2} + \frac{\epsilon}{2} = \epsilon.$$

Hence x and y are equivalent.

The simple proof of our next remark is left for you.

Remark 3.6.   Let (X, d) be a metric space, let C be the set of all Cauchy sequences in X, and let $x, y, z \in C$.   Then

(a) x is equivalent to x.

(b) If x is equivalent to y, then y is equivalent to x.

(c) If x is equivalent to y and y is equivalent to z, then x is equivalent to z.

So the relation "x is equivalent to y" in C of 3.6 is an equivalence relation on C as defined in Ch 1.

Let E be an equivalence relation on some set X, and let $A \subset X$. In Ch 1, we used $E[A]$ to denote $\{x: \ (a, x) \in E$ for some a in $A\}$. In case A is a singleton set $\{p\}$, we abbreviate $E[\{p\}]$ to $E[p]$. For each x in X, the set $E[x]$ is called an *E-equivalence class* (or *equivalence class*). From reflexivity of E, we have

(1) $x \in E[x]$;

and so

(2) $$\bigcup \{E[x]: \quad x \in X\} = X.$$

Now suppose

(3) $$a \in E[b].$$

Then from transitivity of E, $c \in E[a]$ implies $c \in E[b]$; and so

(4) $$E[a] \subset E[b] \quad \text{(if } a \in E[b]).$$

Also (3) and symmetry of E implies $b \in E[a]$; and [just as we proved (4)] (3) implies

$$E[b] \subset E[a].$$

Thus, if b is E-related to a, then $E[a] = E[b]$. Applying this result, we have: If $z \in E[x] \cap E[y]$, then $E[x] = E[z] = E[y]$. Hence:

(5) $$E[x] \cap E[y] = \varnothing \quad \text{or} \quad E[x] = E[y].$$

From (1), (5), and (2), we have:

Remark 3.7.   Let E be an equivalence relation on a set X. Then the collection of all E-equivalence classes is a family of non-void, disjoint sets whose union is X.

Throughout the remainder of this section, let C denote the set of all Cauchy sequences in a fixed metric space (X, d). We shall need:

Exercise 3.8

Let $x, y \in C$, and let S be the sequence in R such that $S_n = d(x_n, y_n)$ for each n in N. Prove that S is a Cauchy sequence. [*Hint* (do not look at this hint unless it is absolutely necessary):

$$d(x_n, y_n) \leq d(x_n, x_m) + d(x_m, y_m) + d(y_m, y_n)$$

so that

$$d(x_n, y_n) - d(x_m, y_m) \leq d(x_n, x_m) + d(y_m, y_n).$$

Similarly,

$$d(x_m, y_m) - d(x_n, y_n) \leq d(x_m, x_n) + d(y_n, y_m).]$$

From 3.8 and 5 in 3.3, we conclude that the S in 3.8 converges to some real number (which is unique for fixed x, y in C, since R is T_2).

For the rest of this section, for x, y in C, let $D(x, y)$ denote the real number to which the sequence S converges, where $S_n = d(x_n, y_n)$.

Remark 3.9.   If $x, y, z \in C$, then

(a) $D(x, y) \geq 0,$

(b) $D(x, y) = 0$ if $x = y,$ and

(c) $D(z, x) \leq D(x, y) + D(y, z).$

We see that D fails to be a metric only because $D(x, y) = 0$ does not imply $x = y$. But, in view of 3.4, we say that x is equivalent to y iff $D(x, y) = 0$. Let $F = \{(x, y): x, y \in C$ and $D(x, y) = 0\}$. In view of 3.6, F is an equivalence relation on C. In the rest of this section, we use C/F to denote $\{F[x]: x \in C\}$, i.e., C/F is the set of all F-equivalence classes. We know that $y \in F[x]$ iff $D(x, y) = 0$.

Remark 3.10.   Let $x, y, z \in C$. If $y \in F[x]$, then $D(x, z) = D(y, z)$.

Proof.   Since $y \in F[x]$, $D(x, y) = D(y, x) = 0$. By 3.9(c),

$$D(z, x) \leq D(x, y) + D(y, z) = D(y, z).$$

Also,

$$D(y, z) \leq D(y, x) + D(x, z) = D(x, z) = D(z, x).$$

Hence

$$D(x, z) = D(y, z).$$

We saw (before 3.7) that for each p in $F[x]$, we have $F[p] = F[x]$; also if $q \in F[z]$, then $F[q] = F[z]$. So from 3.10, we have:

Theorem 3.11.   Let $A, B \in C/F$, $x, y \in A$ and $z, w \in B$. Then

$$D(x, z) = D(y, w).$$

For each pair A, B in C/F, let $e(A, B) = D(x, z)$, where x is an element of A and $z \in B$. In view of 3.11, $e(A, B)$ is determined completely by A and B.

Theorem 3.12.   Let $F[x], F[y], F[z] \in C/F$. Then

(a) $e(F[x], F[y]) \geq 0,$

(b) $e(F[x], F[y]) = 0$ iff $F[x] = F[y],$

(c) $e(F[z], F[x]) \leq e(F[x], F[y]) + e(F[y], F[z]);$

i.e., e is a metric for C/F.

Proof.   Part (a) follows from (a) in 3.9. To prove (b), first suppose $F[x] = F[y]$. Then $(x, y) \in F$, i.e., $D(x, y) = 0$ so that $e(F[x], F[y]) = 0$. Next, suppose $e(F[x], F[y]) = 0$. Then $D(x, y) = 0$, and $y \in F[x]$ so that $F[x] = F[y]$. Part (c) follows from (c) in 3.9.

Exercise 3.13

Let S be a Cauchy sequence in Z where (Z, d) is any metric space. Let T be a sequence in Z, and let P be the sequence in R such that $P_n = d(S_n, T_n)$ for each n in N. Prove: If P converges to 0, then T is a Cauchy sequence and T is equivalent to S.

Theorem 3.14.   The metric space $(C/F, e)$ is complete.

Proof. Let S be a Cauchy sequence in C/F, and let us list the images under S as

$$S: \quad F[x_1], F[x_2], F[x_3], \ldots, F[x_n], \ldots,$$

where (for each n in N) x_n is a *sequence* in our metric space X. Let us list the images under x_i ($i = 1, 2, 3, \ldots, n \ldots$), using $x_i(m)$ to denote the image of m under x_i [$x_i(m)$ being a *point* in X]:

$$x_1: \quad x_1(1), \quad x_1(2), \quad x_1(3), \quad \ldots, \quad x_1(m), \quad \ldots$$

$$x_2: \quad x_2(1), \quad x_2(2), \quad x_2(3), \quad \ldots, \quad x_2(m), \quad \ldots$$

$$\ldots$$

$$x_n: \quad x_n(1), \quad x_n(2), \quad x_n(3), \quad \ldots, \quad x_n(m), \quad \ldots$$

$$\ldots .$$

Since x_n is a Cauchy sequence in X, we know ("taking $\epsilon = 1/n > 0$") there is an integer M_n such that

(α) $d(x_n(i), x_n(M_n)) < 1/n$ for each $i \geq M_n$.

Let y_n be the "constant" Cauchy sequence in X such that $y_n(j) = x_n(M_n)$ for each j in N. Using our usual scheme, we have:

$$y_1: \quad x_1(M_1), \quad x_1(M_1), \quad x_1(M_1), \quad \ldots, \quad x_1(M_1), \quad \ldots$$

$$y_2: \quad x_2(M_2), \quad x_2(M_2), \quad x_2(M_2), \quad \ldots, \quad x_2(M_2), \quad \ldots$$

$$\ldots$$

$$y_n: \quad x_n(M_n), \quad x_n(M_n), \quad x_n(M_n), \quad \ldots, \quad x_n(M_n), \quad \ldots$$

$$\ldots .$$

Let T be the sequence in C/F such that $T_n = F[y_n]$ for each n in N. We see from (α) that $e(F[x_n], F[y_n]) \leq 1/n$. From 3.13, we have that T is a Cauchy sequence in the metric space C/F and that

(β) T is equivalent to S.

Let z be the sequence in X such that $z_n = x_n(M_n)$ for each n in N. To see that T converges to $F[z]$, let $\epsilon > 0$. Since T is Cauchy, there is a k in N such that, if $n, m > k$ then

$$(\gamma) \qquad \epsilon/2 > e(T_n, T_m) = e(F[y_n], F[y_m]) = D(y_n, y_m)$$
$$= d(x_n(M_n), x_m(M_m)) = d(z_n, z_m).$$

Thus z is a Cauchy sequence in X. We also see from (γ) that

$$D(y_n, z) < \epsilon \quad \text{if } n > k$$

[since $d(x_n(M_n), x_m(M_m)) < \epsilon$ if $n, m > k$]. This means that

$$e(F[y_n], F[z]) = e(T_n, F[z]) < \epsilon \quad \text{if } n > k.$$

Hence T converges to $F[z]$. By (β), S is equivalent to T; and by 3.5, S converges to $F[z]$.

Theorem 3.15.   Let $A = \{F[x]: \ x$ is a constant sequence in $X\}$. Then $A^- = C/F$.

Proof. Let $F[y] \in C/F$, and let $\epsilon > 0$. Since y is a Cauchy sequence in X, there is a k in N such that if $m > k$ then $d(y_k, y_m) < \epsilon/2$. Hence

$$e(F[y], F[z]) \leq \frac{\epsilon}{2} < \epsilon,$$

where z is the constant sequence such that $z_n = y_k$ for each n in N (k being the fixed k mentioned in the preceding sentence). But $F[z] \in A$. Hence [7.7(b) in Ch 2] $F[y] \in A^-$. Thus $A^- = C/F$.

Definition 3.16.   Let (Y, d) and (Z, e) be metric spaces and let f be a map of Y onto Z. Then f is called an *isometry* (or *isometric map*) of Y onto Z iff $e(f(x), f(y)) = d(x, y)$ for each pair x, y in Y. Also, Y is said to be *isometric* to Z iff there is an isometry of Y onto Z.

Theorem 3.17.   The metric space (X, d) is isometric to the metric subspace A of C/F in 3.15 [where (X, d) is the fixed metric space of this section].

Proof. For each p in X, let $f(p) = F[z]$, where z is the constant sequence in X such that $z_n = p$ for each n in N. Suppose $p, q \in X$. Clearly

$$e(f(p), f(q)) = d(p, q),$$

and f is an isometry of X onto A (where the metric for A is e restricted to $A \times A$).

When a metric space Y is isometric to a dense subset of a complete metric space Z, then Z is called a *completion* of Y. We see from 3.14, 3.15, and 3.17 that the arbitrary metric space (X, d) has a completion, namely $(C/F, e)$. It is interesting to note that R (the reals) may be developed as C/F in 3.14 (where X is the system of rational numbers) by properly defining the algebraic operations in C/F and the order relation on C/F. Of course, the system of rationals must be developed first.

Exercise 3.18

Prove: If g is an isometry of a metric space (Y, d) onto a metric space (Z, e), then g is a homeomorphism.

4. A Metrization Theorem

Lemma 4.1. For each member t of a dense subset P of the non-negative reals, let A_t be a subset of a set X such that

(a) if $s < t$, then $A_s \subset A_t$ and (b) $\bigcup \{A_t: \ t \in P\} = X$.

For each x in X, let $f(x) = \inf \{t: \ x \in A_t\}$. Then

(1) $\{x: \ f(x) < s\} = \bigcup \{A_t: \ t < s\}$ for each s in R and

(2) $\{x: \ f(x) \le s\} = \bigcap \{A_t: \ t > s\}$ for each real $s \ge 0$.

Proof (1): Suppose $p \in \{x: \ f(x) < s\}$. Then $f(p) < s$, i.e., $\inf \{t: \ p \in A_t\} < s$, and so $p \in A_t$ for some $t < s$. Hence

$$\{x: \ f(x) < s\} \subset \bigcup \{A_t: \ t < s\}.$$

Now suppose $q \in \bigcup \{A_t: \ t < s\}$. Then $q \in A_t$ for some $t < s$, and

$$\inf \{t: \ q \in A_t\} = f(q) < s.$$

So

$$\bigcup \{A_t: \ t < s\} \subset \{x: \ f(x) < s\},$$

and (1) is proved.

(2): Suppose $p \in \{x: \ f(x) \le s\}$, where $s \ge 0$. Let $t_1 \in P$ with $s < t_1$. Then there is some t_2 in P with $t_2 < t_1$ such that $p \in A_{t_2}$ since $f(p) \le s$. Then, by (a), $p \in A_{t_1}$ and hence

$$\{x: \ f(x) \le s\} \subset \bigcap \{A_t: \ t > s\}.$$

Now suppose $q \in \bigcap \{A_t: \ t > s\}$. Then for each y in R with $y > s$, there is a t in P such that $s < t < y$ and such that $q \in A_t$ (since P is dense in the non-negative reals and since $s \ge 0$). Hence $f(q) \le s$, and

$$\bigcap \{A_t: \ t > s\} \subset \{x: \ f(x) \le s\}$$

so that 4.1 is proved.

Lemma 4.2.   For each t in a dense subset P of the non-negative reals, let A_t be an open subset of a topological space X such that

(a)   if $s < t$, then $A_s^- \subset A_t$ and   (b) $\bigcup\{A_t: \ t \in P\} = X$.

The function f such that $f(x) = \inf\{t: \ x \in A_t\}$ is continuous.

Proof.   (We shall use 1.5 in Ch 3, taking the family of all open rays as a subbase for the usual topology for R.)   Let $L_s = \{y: \ y \in R, y < s\}$ be any open left ray in R.   Then $f^{-1}[L_s] = \{x: \ f(x) < s\}$;   and, from (1) in 4.1, this set is the union of open sets and hence is open.   Now let M_s be an open right ray in R (with end point s).   If $s < 0$, then clearly $f^{-1}[M_s] = X$, which is open.   Suppose $s \geq 0$.   Then

$$(3) \qquad X \sim f^{-1}[M_s] = f^{-1}[R \sim M_s] = f^{-1}[\{y: \ y \leq s\}]$$
$$= \{x: \ f(x) \leq s\}$$
$$= \bigcap\{A_t: \ t > s\} \quad \text{by (2) in 4.1.}$$

Clearly

$$\bigcap\{A_t: \ t > s\} \subset \bigcap\{A_t^-: \ t > s\}.$$

Suppose $p \in \bigcap\{A_t^-: \ t > s\}$.   Let t be any element of P with $t > s$.   Since P is dense in the non-negative reals, there is an r in P with $s < r < t$.   So $A_r^- \subset A_t$.   Since $p \in A_r^-$, we have $p \in A_t$.   Hence

$$p \in \bigcap\{A_t: \ t > s\}$$

and

$$(4) \qquad \bigcap\{A_t: \ t > s\} = \bigcap\{A_t^-: \ t > s\}.$$

From (3) and (4), we have $X \sim f^{-1}[M_s]$ is closed if $s \geq 0$.   So for each s in $R, f^{-1}[M_s]$ is open.   By 1.5 in Ch 3, f is continuous.

A *dyadic rational number* is a number of the form $m/2^n$ where m and n are integers.

Remark 4.3.   Let D be the set of all non-negative dyadic rational numbers.   Then D is dense in the set of non-negative reals.

Lemma 4.4 (Urysohn).   If X is a normal topological space, then for each pair of non-void disjoint closed subsets A and B of X, there is a continuous map f of X into Q (where $Q = [0, 1]$) such that $f[A] = \{0\}$ and $f[B] = \{1\}$.

Proof.   Let D be the set of all non-negative dyadic rationals.   By 5.10(a) in Ch 4, let U_0 be an open set such that

$$(5) \qquad A \subset U_0 \quad \text{and} \quad U_0^- \subset X \sim B.$$

Let

(6) $$U_1 = X \sim B.$$

Again by 5.10(a) in Ch 4, let $U_{1/2}$ be an open set such that

$$U_0^- \subset U_{1/2} \quad \text{and} \quad U_{1/2}^- \subset U_1.$$

Let $U_{1/4}$ and $U_{3/4}$ be open sets such that

$$U_0^- \subset U_{1/4}, \quad U_{1/4}^- \subset U_{1/2}, \quad U_{1/2}^- \subset U_{3/4} \quad \text{and} \quad U_{3/4}^- \subset U_1.$$

Now let $U_{i/8}$ ($i = 1, 3, 5, 7$) be open sets such that

$$U_0^- \subset U_{1/8}, \quad U_{1/8}^- \subset U_{1/4}, \quad U_{1/4}^- \subset U_{3/8}, \quad U_{3/8}^- \subset U_{1/2}, \quad U_{1/2}^- \subset U_{5/8},$$

$$U_{5/8}^- \subset U_{3/4}, \quad U_{3/4}^- \subset U_{7/8} \quad \text{and} \quad U_{7/8}^- \subset U_1.$$

By induction, for each t in $D \cap [0, 1]$, we may let U_t be an open set such that: (5) and (6) hold and if $r, t \in D \cap [0, 1]$ with $r < t$ then $U_r^- \subset U_t$.

Finally, let

(7) $$U_t = X \quad \text{for each } t \text{ in } D \text{ with } t > 1.$$

So,

(8) $$\text{if } r, t \in D \text{ with } r < t, \quad \text{then } U_r^- \subset U_t.$$

For each x in X, let $f(x) = \inf \{t: \ t \in D \text{ and } x \in U_t\}$. By 4.2 and 4.3, f is continuous. By (5), $f[A] = \{0\}$. By (6), (7) and (8), $f[B] = \{1\}$. Clearly $f[X] \subset Q$.

Embedding Theorem 4.5.   Each regular second countable T_1 space $(X, \mathcal{T})$ is homeomorphic to a subspace of the Hilbert space H in 7.10 of Ch 2.

Proof.   Let $\mathcal{B}$ be a countable base for $\mathcal{T}$, and let

$$\mathcal{C} = \{(U, V): \ U, V \in \mathcal{B} \quad \text{and} \quad U^- \subset V\}.$$

Since $\mathcal{C}$ is countable, let S be a map of N onto $\mathcal{C}$ and denote S_n by (U_n, V_n). By 6.7 in Ch 4, X is normal. By 4.4, for each n in N, let f_n be a continuous map of X into Q such that $f_n(x) = 0$ if $x \in U_n^-$ and $f_n(x) = 1$ if $x \in X \sim V_n$. For each x in X, let

$$g(x) = (f_1(x), f_2(x)/2, f_3(x)/3, \ldots, f_n(x)/n, \ldots).$$

Clearly $g(x) \in H$. To see that g is one-to-one, suppose $x \neq y$ in X. Since X is regular and T_2, there is a member (U_i, V_i) of $\mathcal{C}$ such that $x \in U_i$ and $y \notin V_i$. So $f_i(x) = 0$ and $f_i(y) = 1$. Hence $g(x) \neq g(y)$.

To see that g is continuous at an arbitrary point p in X, let $\epsilon > 0$. Let $k \in N$ such that for each x in X,

$$\sum_{k+1}^{\infty} \frac{[f_n(p) - f_n(x)]^2}{n^2} < \frac{\epsilon^2}{2}.$$

For each $n \leq k$, (since f_n is continuous) let W_n be a neighborhood of p such that for x in W_n,

$$\frac{[f_n(p) - f_n(x)]^2}{n^2} < \frac{\epsilon^2}{2k} .$$

Now the set $W = W_1 \cap W_2 \cap \ldots \cap W_k$ is a neighborhood of p such that if $x \in W$, then

$$[d(g(p), g(x))]^2 = \sum_1^k \frac{[f_n(p) - f_n(x)]^2}{n^2}$$

$$+ \sum_{k+1}^\infty \frac{[f_n(p) - f_n(x)]^2}{n^2} < \frac{k\epsilon^2}{2k} + \frac{\epsilon^2}{2} = \epsilon^2.$$

Hence g is continuous.

Suppose A is open in X and $q \in g[A]$. Let $p \in A$ such that $g(p) = q$. Let $(U_k, V_k) \in \mathcal{C}$ such that $p \in U_k$ and $U_k^- \subset V_k \subset A$. Then $f_k(p) = 0$ and $f_k(x) = 1$ if $x \notin A$. Hence if $x \notin A$, then

$$d(g(p), g(x)) \geq \frac{|f_k(p) - f_k(x)|}{k} = \frac{1}{k} .$$

This means $g[X] \cap S_r(q) \subset g[A]$, where r is any positive radius less than $1/k$. Therefore $g[A]$ is open in the subspace $g[X]$ of H. So g is a homeomorphism of X onto the subspace $g[X]$.

We recall that a space $(X, \mathcal{T})$ is called *metrizable* iff there is a metric d for X such that the d-metric topology is $\mathcal{T}$.

Remark 4.6.   If a space $(X, \mathcal{T})$ is homeomorphic to a subspace of a metric space (Y, d), then $(X, \mathcal{T})$ is metrizable.

Proof. Let h be a homeomorphism of X onto a subspace of Y. For p, q in X, let $e(p, q) = d(h(p), h(q))$. Clearly e is a metric for X which induces $\mathcal{T}$.

The following is a corollary of 4.5 and 4.6:

Urysohn Metrization Theorem 4.7.   Each regular second countable T_1 space is metrizable.

It follows from 4.7 that each regular second countable T_1 space is a separable metrizable space. We also know that each separable metric space is regular, second countable and T_1. So:

Theorem 4.8.   A space is separable and metrizable iff it is regular, second countable and T_1.

The last theorem is a characterization of separable metric spaces. But there are metric spaces which are not separable. So 4.8 is not a characterization of general metric spaces. For a general metrization theorem, you may see Kelley's *General Topology*.

7

More on Product Spaces
and Function Spaces

1. Compactness in Terms of Subbases

One of the most important theorems of general topology is the Tychonoff theorem, which states that the product of compact spaces is compact. A simple proof of this theorem is given in the next section. While looking forward to that proof, we devote this section to some preliminaries necessary to the proof.

We stated in section 5 of Ch 3 that the Hausdorff Maximal Principle is equivalent to the Axiom of Choice. In order to state this Maximal Principle (which could have been adopted as an axiom instead of the Choice Axiom), we need some definitions.

Definition 1.1.   Let $\leq$ be a binary relation on a set X. Then $\leq$ is called a *partial ordering in* X (or X is *partially ordered* by $\leq$) iff (a) $\leq$ is transitive, and (b) $x \leq y$ and $y \leq x$ implies $x = y$.

Definition 1.2.   Let $\leq$ be a partial ordering in a set X, and let $Y \subset X$.
(a) Y is *simply ordered* by $\leq$ iff $x, y \in Y$ with $y \neq x$ implies $x \leq y$ or $y \leq x$.

(b) In particular, $\leq$ is a *simple ordering* in X iff X is simply ordered by $\leq$.

[Many writers require that a partial ordering be reflexive;   some do not. We choose not to do so in this book, in order that the "strict less than" relation $<$ (in R, N, and other sets) be a simple ordering (and hence a partial ordering).]

Remark 1.3.   Let C be a family of subsets of a set Z.   For $A, B \in C$, let us say $A \leq B$ iff $A \subset B$.   Then $\leq$ partially orders C.

A collection C of sets is said to be *ordered by set inclusion* iff C is assigned the partial ordering of 1.3.   When we use an order in a family of sets without specifying the order relation, it is understood that the collection is ordered by set inclusion.

Axiom 1.4 (Hausdorff Maximal Principle, or HMP).   If A is a simply ordered subset of a partially ordered set X, then there is a maximal simply ordered set Y such that $A \subset Y \subset X$.

By a maximal simply ordered set Y, we mean: Y is simply ordered; and if $Y \subset Z \subset X$, where Z is simply ordered, then $Z = Y$.
As an example, we may partially order the set E_2 so that

$$(x, y) \leq (a, b) \text{ iff } x < a.$$

(Note that two elements with the same first coordinate are not comparable in this ordering.)   Let

$$A = \{(x, y): \quad x \in N \quad \text{and} \quad y = 3\}.$$

Then A is a simply ordered subset of E_2.   By 1.4, we know there is at least one maximal simply ordered subset of E_2 containing A.   In this example, we can notice many such sets.   One is

$$\{(x, y): \quad x \in R \quad \text{and} \quad y = 3\}.$$

Another is

$$\{(x, y): \quad x \in R, y = 3 \text{ if } \quad x \in N, \quad \text{and} \quad y = 4 \text{ if } \quad x \notin N\}.$$

We repeat that 1.4 may be proved with the aid of the Axiom of Choice. Also 1.4 implies the Choice Axiom.   So either statement could be taken as an axiom.   (Then the other follows.)   As this is not a book on the foundations of mathematics, we do not wish to prove either implication.

Remark I.5.   Let $a \in X$, where X is a partially ordered set. Then there is a maximal simply ordered set Y in X such that $a \in Y$.

Proof. The singleton set $\{a\}$ is a trivial simply ordered set. Hence, by HMP, there is a maximal simply ordered set Y such that $\{a\} \subset Y$.

Lemma I.6.   Let $(X, \mathcal{T})$ be a topological space, and let $\mathfrak{D}$ be a maximal finitely short family of open sets. If some member of $\mathfrak{D}$ contains $G_1 \cap G_2 \cap \ldots \cap G_n$, where each G_i is open, then $G_k \in \mathfrak{D}$ for some k in N_n.

Proof. First suppose $n = 2$. Suppose $G_1 \notin \mathfrak{D}$ and $G_2 \notin \mathfrak{D}$. Then, by maximality of $\mathfrak{D}$, there must be members $A_1, A_2, \ldots, A_p$ of $\mathfrak{D}$ such that

$$G_1 \cup A_1 \cup A_2 \cup \ldots \cup A_p = X.$$

Also, there are members $B_1, B_2, \ldots, B_q$ of $\mathfrak{D}$ such that

$$G_2 \cup B_1 \cup B_2 \cup \ldots \cup B_q = X.$$

Then

$$(G_1 \cap G_2) \cup A_1 \cup A_2 \cup \ldots \cup A_p \cup B_1 \cup B_2 \cup \ldots \cup B_q = X,$$

so that no member of $\mathfrak{D}$ can contain $G_1 \cap G_2$. We have proved the contrapositive of 1.6 for $n = 2$. Similarly, we conclude 1.6 is valid where n is any positive integer.

Lemma I.7.   Let $\mathcal{F}$ be a finitely short subfamily of $\mathcal{T}$, where $(X, \mathcal{T})$ is a topological space. Then there is a maximal finitely short subfamily $\mathfrak{D}$ of $\mathcal{T}$ such that $\mathcal{F} \subset \mathfrak{D}$.

Proof. Let $\mathcal{C}$ be the collection of all finitely short subfamilies of $\mathcal{T}$, and let $\mathcal{C}$ be ordered by set inclusion. [Thus if $\mathcal{C}_1, \mathcal{C}_2 \in \mathcal{C}$, then $\mathcal{C}_1 \leq \mathcal{C}_2$ iff $\mathcal{C}_1 \subset \mathcal{C}_2$, i.e., $\mathcal{C}_1$ is a subfamily of $\mathcal{C}_2$.] Now $\mathcal{F} \in \mathcal{C}$. So, by 1.5, let $\mathcal{A}$ be a maximal simply ordered subcollection of $\mathcal{C}$ such that $\mathcal{F} \in \mathcal{A}$. Let $\mathfrak{D} = \bigcup \mathcal{A}$. [The union of $\mathcal{A}$ is a family of open sets, since each member of $\mathcal{A}$ is such a family.] We shall show: (1) $\mathfrak{D}$ is finitely short and (2) $\mathfrak{D}$ is a maximal finitely short subfamily of $\mathcal{T}$.

To prove (1), let $D_1, D_2, \ldots, D_k \in \mathfrak{D}$. Then, for each i in N_k, there is some $\mathcal{C}_i$ in $\mathcal{A}$ such that $D_i \in \mathcal{C}_i$. Since $\mathcal{A}$ is simply ordered, one of these $\mathcal{C}_i$'s, say $\mathcal{C}_j$, contains each of the other $\mathcal{C}_i$'s; and so $D_i \in \mathcal{C}_j$ for each i in N_k. Thus $D_1 \cup D_2 \cup \ldots \cup D_k \neq X$, since $\mathcal{C}_j$ is finitely short. Hence $\mathfrak{D}$ is finitely short.

Now suppose (2) were not true; i.e., suppose there were some open set $G \notin \mathfrak{D}$ such that $\mathfrak{D} \cup \{G\}$ is still finitely short. Then $\mathcal{A} \cup \{\mathfrak{D} \cup \{G\}\}$ would be simply ordered (since $\mathfrak{D}$ contains each member of $\mathcal{A}$) and would properly contain $\mathcal{A}$ (since $G \notin \mathfrak{D} = \bigcup \mathcal{A}$), contradicting the maximality of $\mathcal{A}$. Thus (2) must be true, and $\mathfrak{D}$ is the required maximal finitely short family containing $\mathcal{F}$. [$\mathcal{F} \subset \mathfrak{D}$ since $\mathcal{F} \in \mathcal{A}$ and $\mathfrak{D} = \bigcup \mathcal{A}$.]

Theorem 1.8.   Let $\mathcal{S}$ be a subbase for $\mathcal{T}$, where $(X, \mathcal{T})$ is a topological space. If each cover for X by members of $\mathcal{S}$ has a finite subcover for X, then X is compact.

Proof. [We shall show: Each finitely short subfamily of $\mathcal{T}$ is short. This implies X is compact (1.11 in Ch 4).] Let $\mathcal{F}$ be any finitely short subfamily of $\mathcal{T}$. By 1.7, let $\mathcal{D}$ be a maximal finitely short subfamily of $\mathcal{T}$ which contains $\mathcal{F}$. [We shall show that $\mathcal{D}$ is short, which certainly implies $\mathcal{F}$ is short.]

The subfamily $\mathcal{D} \cap \mathcal{S}$ of $\mathcal{D}$ is finitely short (since $\mathcal{D}$ is finitely short). So, by hypothesis, $\mathcal{D} \cap \mathcal{S}$ is short;   i.e.,

(1) $\bigcup(\mathcal{D} \cap \mathcal{S}) \neq X.$

Now suppose $p \in \bigcup \mathcal{D}$. Then $p \in V$ for some V in $\mathcal{D}$. Since V is open (and $\mathcal{S}$ is a subbase),

$$p \in G_1 \cap G_2 \cap \ldots \cap G_k \subset V$$

for some G_i's in $\mathcal{S}$. By 1.6, $G_j \in \mathcal{D}$ for some j in N_k. So $p \in G_j \in \mathcal{D} \cap \mathcal{S}$. Hence

$$p \in \bigcup (\mathcal{D} \cap \mathcal{S}), \quad \text{and} \quad \bigcup \mathcal{D} \subset \bigcup (\mathcal{D} \cap \mathcal{S}).$$

So from (1), we have $\mathcal{D}$ is short.   Hence $\mathcal{F}$ is short, and X is compact.

2. The Tychonoff Theorem

Theorem 2.1 (Tychonoff Theorem).   If $\{(X_a, \mathcal{T}_a): \ a \in A\}$ is a collection of compact spaces, then the product space $\times \{X_a: \ a \in A\}$ is compact.

Proof. Let $\mathcal{S}$ be the defining subbase for the product topology, i.e.,

$$\mathcal{S} = \{f_a^{-1}[U_a]: \ U_a \in \mathcal{T}_a, a \in A\},$$

and let $\mathcal{F}$ be a finitely short subfamily of $\mathcal{S}$. For a in A, let

$$\mathcal{B}_a = \{U_a: \ f_a^{-1}[U_a] \in \mathcal{F} \}.$$

Then $\mathcal{B}_a$ is finitely short in X_a. (Otherwise $\mathcal{F}$ would not be finitely short in $\times \{X_a: \ a \in A\}$.) Since X_a is compact, $\mathcal{B}_a$ does not cover X_a. So for each a in A, let $x_a \in X_a \sim \bigcup \mathcal{B}_a$. Now let x be the point in $\times \{X_a: \ a \in A\}$ whose ath coordinate is x_a for each a in A. Clearly $x \notin \bigcup \mathcal{F}$, and $\mathcal{F}$ is short. By 1.8, $\times \{X_a: \ a \in A\}$ is compact.

Corollary 2.2 (Heine-Borel Theorem for E_n).   A subset A of E_n is compact iff A is closed and bounded.

Proof. If A is compact, then A is closed and bounded, since E_n is a metric space. Suppose A is closed and bounded. Then $f_i[A]$ is bounded in R for each i in N_n. So, for each i in N_n, let B_i be a closed interval in R such that $f_i[A] \subset B_i$. Each B_i is compact, and, by 2.1, $\times \{B_i: \quad i \in N_n\}$ is a compact subset of E_n (with due consideration of relative topologies and the relation between compact subsets and compact subspaces). Now, since A is a closed subset of $\times \{B_i: \quad i \in N\}$, it follows that A is compact [1(a) in 3.6 of Ch 3].

Is the converse of 2.1 true?

3. Tychonoff Cubes

Suppose for each a in an index set A, X_a denotes the closed unit interval

$$Q = \{x: \quad x \in R \text{ and } 0 \leq x \leq 1\}$$

with the usual topology. Then the product space $\times \{X_a: \quad a \in A\}$ is called a *Tychonoff cube*. We have immediately (from previous results in this book):

Theorem 3.1.   Each Tychonoff cube is normal.

If after several minutes you have not been able to prove 3.1, then see 6.3 in Ch 4, 3.5 in Ch 5, and the Tychonoff Theorem.

We recall that if for each a in an index set A, X_a is a set, then the Cartesian product set $\times \{X_a: \quad a \in A\}$ is the set of all maps x defined on A such that $x(a) \in X_a$ for each a in A. Also, for a given a in A, the ath projection map is the map f_a of $\times \{X_a: \quad a \in A\}$ into X_a such that $f_a(x) = x(a)$ for the fixed a. Throughout the rest of this chapter, let us use P_a to denote the ath projection map, and let us use f (rather than x) to denote a typical element in $\times \{X_a: \quad a \in A\}$.

Our main concern in this section is with one specific Tychonoff cube—the one obtained when the index set A is also Q. If for each a in Q, $X_a = Q$, then the Cartesian product set $\times \{X_a: \quad a \in Q\}$ is just the set of all maps of Q into Q, i.e., $\{f: \quad f \text{ is a map of } Q \text{ into } Q\}$.

In general, if A and B are sets, then $\{f: \quad f \text{ is a map of } B \text{ into } A\}$ is denoted by A^B. So we shall use Q^Q to denote $\times \{X_a: \quad a \in Q\}$ when $X_a = Q$ for each a in Q. Further, when we use Q^Q as a space without specifying a topology, the product topology is understood.

Since a member f of Q^Q is just a function on Q to Q, it is convenient to think of f (or its ordinary graph) as a subset of the unit square $Q \times Q$. Pictorially, what does a member of the defining subbase for the product topology for Q^Q look like?

If V is one of these subbase members, then $V = P_a^{-1}[V_a]$ for some a in Q and some open set V_a in $X_a (= Q)$. So V is the set of all elements (functions) in Q^Q each of which has its ath coordinate restricted to lie in V_a.

Now V_a, being open in Q, is the union of open intervals in Q (unless 0 or 1 belongs to V_a). Thus a typical subbase member V may be described by: A map f of Q into Q belongs to V iff (the graph of) f passes through one of the open interval gaps in the vertical line erected at a in Figure 1. A typical base member B may be described by: An f in Q^Q belongs to B iff f passes through one of the open interval gaps over each a_i in a finite subset of Q in Figure 2.

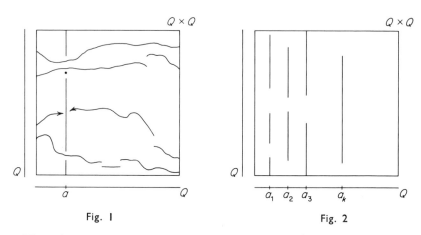

Fig. 1   Fig. 2

Now that we are quite familiar with the space Q^Q, let us show that it is not completely normal. For $a \in Q$, let g_a denote the characteristic function for a, that is, $g_a(a) = 1$ while $g_a(r) = 0$ if $r \in Q \sim \{a\}$. In the following exercises, let $A = \{g_a: \ a \in Q$ and a is rational$\}$ and let $B = \{g_a: \ a \in Q$ and a is irrational$\}$. Also let $o \in Q^Q$ such that $o(r) = 0$ for each r in Q.

Exercises 3.2

1. Prove $o \in A' \cap B'$ in the space Q^Q. (o, A, and B given above.)

2. Let $f \in Q^Q \sim \{o\}$. Prove $f \notin (A \cup B)'$.

3. Prove A and B are separated.

4. Prove there do not exist disjoint open sets about A and B respectively.

We have from 3.1 and 3.2:

Remark 3.3. Q^Q is a normal space which is not completely normal.

The proof of 1 in 3.2 is not awkward at all. Let U be a neighborhood of o. Then U contains a base member W such that $o \in W$. (See Figure 3.)

Let $F = \{b, c, d, \ldots, k\}$ be the finite subset of Q such that for each a in F, the ath coordinates of members of W are restricted to lie in an open set U_a in Q while all other coordinates of members of W are "unrestricted" (except that they must be in Q). For each a in F, the restricting U_a must contain 0 (since $o \in W$). Since F is finite while the set of rationals in Q is infinite, we may let p be a rational in $Q \sim F$. Then $g_p \in W$ and $g_p \neq o$. Hence $o \in A'$. Similarly $o \in B'$.

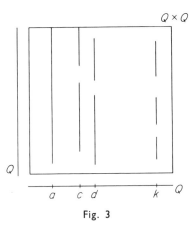

$Q \times Q$

Fig. 3

To prove 4, let U and V be *any* open sets in Q^Q such that $A \subset U$ and $B \subset V$. Let D be the set of all rationals in Q; and for each r in D, let W_r be a base member such that $g_r \in W_r \subset U$. For each r in D, let F_r be the finite set in Q such that $P_a[W_r] = Q$ if $a \in Q \sim F_r$. Since $\bigcup \{F_r : r \in D\}$ is countable (while the set of irrationals in Q is uncountable), we may let s be some irrational in $Q \sim \bigcup \{F_r : r \in D\}$. Now let F_s be a finite set in Q such that the base member $\times \{V_a : a \in Q\}$ (where $V_a = Q$ if $a \in Q \sim F_s$) contains g_s and is contained in V. Let t be a rational in $Q \sim F_s$. Let g be the element of Q^Q such that $g(x) = 1$ if $x = s$ or $x = t$ while $g(x) = 0$ otherwise. Clearly $g \in U \cap V$ (since $s \notin \bigcup \{F_r : r \in D\}$ and $t \notin F_s$). Since U and V were *any* open sets about A and B, it follows that there are no disjoint open sets about A and B respectively.

Exercises 3.4

1. Let X be the product space $\times \{X_a : a \in A\}$. For $z \in X$ and $c \in A$, let
$$L_z(c) = \{x : x \in X \text{ and } x(a) = z(a) \text{ if } a \neq c\}.$$
Prove: The restriction of P_c to $L_z(c)$ is a homeomorphism of $L_z(c)$ onto X_c.

2. Suppose each X_a in 1 is connected and $x, y \in X$ such that $x_a = y_a$ except for a finite set F in A. Prove there is a connected set K in X such that $x, y \in K$.

3. Prove: If each X_a in 1 is connected, then X is connected. [*Hint*: Suppose x is a fixed point in X. Let $Y = \{y:$ there is a connected subset of X containing both y and $x\}$. Use 2 to show that each neighborhood of a point p in X contains points of the connected set Y. Thus $Y^- = X$ and X is connected. (1 in 5.8 of Ch 2 shows that Y is connected.)]

To prove 2, let $F = \{c_1, c_2, \ldots, c_n\}$ be the finite set in A such that $x(c_i) \neq y(c_i)$. Let $p_1 \in L_x(c_1)$ such that $p_1(c_1) = y(c_1)$ (using the notation in 1). By 1, $L_x(c_1)$ and $L_{p_1}(c_2)$ are connected since X_{c_1} and X_{c_2} are connected. Since $p_1 \in L_x(c_1) \cap L_{p_1}(c_2)$, 1 in 5.8 of Ch 2 implies $L_x(c_1) \cup L_{p_1}(c_2)$ is connected. Then let

$$p_2 \in L_{p_1}(c_2) \quad \text{such that} \quad p_2(c_2) = y(c_2),$$

$$p_3 \in L_{p_2}(c_3) \quad \text{such that} \quad p_3(c_3) = y(c_3),$$

$$\cdots$$

$$p_{n-1} \in L_{p_{n-2}}(c_{n-1}) \quad \text{such that} \quad p_{n-1}(c_{n-1}) = y(c_{n-1})$$

and conclude that

$$L_x(c_1) \cup L_{p_1}(c_2) \cup \ldots \cup L_{p_{n-1}}(c_n)$$

is connected and contains x and y since $x \in L_x(c_1)$ and $y \in L_{p_{n-1}}(c_n)$.

4. Tychonoff Spaces

Intermediate between T_3 and T_4 spaces, we have an important type of space.

Definition 4.1.   (a) A topological space X is *completely regular* iff for each $p \in X$ and each neighborhood U of p, there is a continuous map f of X into Q such that $f(p) = 0$ and $f(x) = 1$ if $x \in X \sim U$.

(b) A space is *Tychonoff* iff it is T_1 and completely regular.

Urysohn's Lemma gives us at once the result that each T_4 space is a Tychonoff space. Hence each metric space is Tychonoff. The simple proof that each Tychonoff space is T_3 is left for you.

Remark 4.2. Let S be a subbase for $\mathcal{T}$, where $(X, \mathcal{T})$ is a space. If for each V in S and each p in V there is a continuous map f of X into Q such that $f(p) = 0$ and $f[X \sim V] \subset \{1\}$, then X is completely regular.

Proof. Suppose $p \in X$ and U is a neighborhood of p. Then (unless $U = X$, a trivial case) there are members $V_1, V_2, \ldots, V_k$ of S such that

$$p \in V_1 \cap V_2 \cap \ldots \cap V_k \subset U.$$

For each i in N_k, let $f_i\colon X \longrightarrow Q$ be a continuous map such that $f_i(p) = 0$ and $f_i(x) = 1$ if $x \in X \sim V_i$. Let $f\colon X \longrightarrow Q$ be defined such that $f(x) = \max \{f_i(x)\colon i \in N_k\}$. Clearly $f(p) = 0$ and $f(x) = 1$ if $x \in X \sim U$. It is easy to see that f is continuous. [In case $k = 2$,

$$f(x) = \frac{|f_1(x) + f_2(x)|}{2} + \frac{|f_1(x) - f_2(x)|}{2}$$

(since $f_i(x) \geq 0$). So 1.12 in Ch 3 (and the fact that $g\colon X \longrightarrow R$ is continuous implies $|g|$ is continuous—where $|g|(x) = |g(x)|$) may be used to conclude that f is continuous in case $k = 2$. By induction, f is continuous.]

Theorem 4.3. If for each a in A, X_a is a Tychonoff space, then the product space $X = \times \{X_a\colon a \in A\}$ is Tychonoff.

Proof. X is T_1 by 1 in 3.14 of Ch 5. So let V be a member of the usual subbase for the product topology, and suppose $x \in V$. Then $V = P_a^{-1}[U]$, where U is a neighborhood of x_a for some a. Let $g\colon X_a \longrightarrow Q$ be continuous and such that $g(x_a) = 0$ and $g(z) = 1$ if $z \in X_a \sim U$. Then $g \circ P_a$ is the desired map and X is Tychonoff by 4.2.

Definition 4.4. Let $\mathcal{F}$ be a family of functions, each on a fixed space X. For each f in $\mathcal{F}$, let Y_f be a space such that f is a map of X into Y_f. Let $Z = \times \{Y_f\colon f \in \mathcal{F}\}$ and let Z have the product topology.

(a) Let $e\colon X \longrightarrow Z$ be such that for x in X, $e(x)$ is the point in Z whose fth coordinate is $f(x)$ for each f in $\mathcal{F}$. This map e is called the *evaluation map for $\mathcal{F}$*.

(b) $\mathcal{F}$ is said to separate points iff e is one-to-one [that is, $x, y \in X$ with $x \neq y$ implies there is some f in $\mathcal{F}$ such that $f(x) \neq f(y)$].

(c) $\mathcal{F}$ *separates points and closed sets* iff for each closed subset H of X and each point p in $X \sim H$, there is an f in $\mathcal{F}$ such that $f(p) \notin (f[H])^-$.

Theorem 4.5. (a) If each f in 4.4 is continuous, then e is continuous.
(b) If the $\mathcal{F}$ in 4.4 separates points and closed sets, then e is an open map of X onto the subspace $e[X]$ of Z.

Proof. (a) Since $P_f \circ e = f$, the continuity of e follows from 3.7 in Ch 5.

(b) Let G be an open subset of X. Suppose $q \in e[G]$ and let $p \in G$ such that $e(p) = q$. Let $f \in \mathscr{F}$ such that

$$f(p) \notin (f[X \sim G])^- \quad \text{in } Y_f$$

(since $\mathscr{F}$ separates points and closed sets). Let

$$U = Y_f \sim (f[X \sim G])^-.$$

Then $P_f^{-1}[U]$ (a subbase member of the product topology) is open in Z. Let

$$V = e[X] \cap P_f^{-1}[U].$$

Then V is open in the subspace $e[X]$, $e(p) = q \in V$ and $V \subset e[G]$. Hence e is an open map of X onto the subspace $e[X]$.

From 4.5, we now have:

Theorem 4.6.   If the $\mathscr{F}$ in 4.4 separates points and separates points and closed sets while each f is continuous, then e is a homeomorphism of X onto the subspace $e[X]$ of Z.

It is easy for you to prove:

Remark 4.7.   The property of being a Tychonoff space is (a) hereditary and (b) a topological invariant.

As observed after 4.1, each metric space is Tychonoff. So Q is Tychonoff. Hence, by 4.3:

Theorem 4.8.   Each Tychonoff cube is a Tychonoff space.

Further, we have the following characterization of a Tychonoff space.

Theorem 4.9.   A space X is a Tychonoff space iff X is homeomorphic to a subspace of a Tychonoff cube.

Proof. The if part follows from 4.7 and 4.8. To prove the other half, let $\mathscr{F}$ be the family of all continuous maps of X into Q. Since X is completely regular, $\mathscr{F}$ separates points and closed sets. Since X is completely regular and T_1, $\mathscr{F}$ separates points. Hence, by 4.6, X is homeomorphic to a subspace of the cube $Q^{\mathscr{F}}$.

5. A Second Proof of Urysohn's Metrization Theorem

Theorem 4.6 not only leads us to a characterization of Tychonoff spaces, but also gives us a most elegant proof of Urysohn's metrization theorem.

Theorem 5.1. Each second countable regular T_1 space $(X, \mathcal{T})$ is homeomorphic to a subspace of a metrizable (Tychonoff) cube (and hence is metrizable).

Proof. Let $\mathcal{B}$ be a countable base for $\mathcal{T}$, and let $\mathcal{C}$ be the set of all pairs (U, V) such that $U, V \in \mathcal{B}$ and $U^- \subset V$. Since $\mathcal{C}$ is countable, $\mathcal{C}$ may be written as $\{(U_n, V_n): n \in N\}$. By 6.7 in Ch 4, X is normal and 4.4 in Ch 6 gives for each n in N a continuous map f_n of X into Q such that $f_n(x) = 0$ if $x \in U_n^-$ and $f_n(x) = 1$ if $x \in X \sim V_n$. Let $\mathcal{F} = \{f_n: n \in N\}$. Suppose H is a closed subset of X and $p \in X \sim H$. Then there is a V in $\mathcal{B}$ such that $p \in V \subset X \sim H$. Since X is regular, there is (by 5.9 in Ch 4) an open set W such that $p \in W$ and $W^- \subset V$. So there is a U in $\mathcal{B}$ such that $p \in U \subset W$ and $U^- \subset W^- \subset V$. The pair $(U, V) = (U_k, V_k) \in \mathcal{C}$ for some k in N. Now

$$f_k(p) = 0 \notin \{1\} \supset (f_k[X \sim V_k])^- \supset (f_k[H])^-,$$

for $H \subset X \sim V_k$ since $V_k \subset X \sim H$. Hence $\mathcal{F}$ separates points and closed sets. This implies $\mathcal{F}$ separates points also (since X is T_1). By 4.6, X is homeomorphic to a subspace of $Q^{\mathcal{F}}$. But $Q^{\mathcal{F}}$ is metrizable (by 2.6 in Ch 6) since $\mathcal{F}$ is countable.

6. Ordinal Numbers

Spaces involving ordinal numbers provide some most interesting and instructive examples. So let us digress briefly and discuss ordinal numbers. If $\leq$ is a partial ordering in a set X, we shall write $x < y$ iff $x \leq y$ and $x \neq y$. We shall say x is less than y iff $x < y$. (We also use $\geq$ and $>$ just as expected.) If A is a subset of a simply ordered set, then a is called the *least* (or *first*) *element of* A iff (1) $a \in A$ and (2) $b \in A \sim \{a\}$ implies $a < b$.

Definition 6.1. A simple ordering $\leq$ in a set X is said to *well-order* X (or X *is well-ordered* by $\leq$) iff each non-void subset A of X has a least element.

The set R is not well-ordered by the usual ordering in R, for the open interval $(0, 1)$ has no first element. The set N is well-ordered by its usual ordering.

Two partially ordered sets X and Y are said to be *order isomorphic* (or *of the same order type* or *similar*) iff there is a one-to-one map of X onto Y which preserves order. Such a map is called an *(order) isomorphism*. Clearly, the relation of being similar is reflexive, symmetric and transitive. The set N is similar to $N \sim \{1\}$ as well as to the set of all even positive integers. So a well-ordered set may be similar to a proper subset of itself. But:

Remark 6.2.   If f is an isomorphism of a well-ordered set X onto a subset of X, then (for a given x in X)

$$f(x) > x \quad \text{or} \quad f(x) = x.$$

Proof. Let $A = \{x: \ f(x) < x\}$. (We want to show $A = \varnothing$.) Suppose $A \neq \varnothing$. Since X is well-ordered, let p be the first element of A. Then $f(p) < p$; and since f preserves order, $f(f(p)) < f(p)$—contradicting the assumption that p was the first element of X such that $f(p) < p$. [$f(f(p)) \neq f(p)$ since f is one-to-one while $f(p) < p$ so that $f(p) \neq p$ (and hence $f(f(p)) \neq f(p)$).]

Let $p \in X$, where X is well-ordered. The set $\{x: \ x \in X \text{ and } x < p\}$ is called the *section from p* and is denoted by $L(p)$.

Corollary 6.3.   A well-ordered set X cannot be similar to a section in X.

Theorem 6.4 (Principle of Transfinite Induction).   Let X be a well-ordered set.   If $A \subset X$ such that

(1) $x \in X$ and $L(x) \subset A$ implies $x \in A$,

then $A = X$.

Proof. Suppose $A \neq X$. Then $X \sim A \neq \varnothing$. Let p be the least element of $X \sim A$. Then $p \in X$, $L(p) \subset A$ but $p \notin A$—contradicting (1). We conclude $A = X$.

Remark 6.5.   If X and Y are well-ordered sets, then

(a) X is similar to Y, X is similar to some section $L(y)$ in Y, or Y is similar to some section $L(x)$ in X, and

(b) exactly one of the three alternatives in (a) holds.

If X or Y in 6.5 is void, the conclusion is clear. If neither set is void, we map the first element of one set onto the first element of the other. If this does not exhaust either set, we may map the second element of one set onto the second element of the other. By the principle of transfinite induction, a one-to-one map exists which exhausts one of the sets X or Y and which preserves order. Hence (a) follows. Corollary 6.3 may be used to prove (b). [If $f: \ X \longrightarrow L(y)$ were an isomorphism and $g: \ Y \longrightarrow L(x)$ an isomorphism, then $g \circ f$ would be an isomorphism of X onto $L(x)$—contradicting 6.3.]

Since the relation, among well-ordered sets, of being similar is reflexive, transitive and symmetric, this relation is an equivalence relation;   and two well-ordered sets X and Y belong to the same equivalence class iff X and Y

are order isomorphic. A given well-ordered set X determines the equivalence class of all well-ordered sets similar to X. We may call this equivalence class the *ordinal number* or *order type* which has X as a representative. If we use α to denote this ordinal number, then we say X is of order type α.

Let $k \in N$, and let X and Y be any two well-ordered sets each consisting of exactly k elements. Then X and Y are similar. Thus it is natural to use k to denote the ordinal number determined by X. Also, $\varnothing \times \varnothing$ is a binary relation on $\varnothing$ which is a well-ordering in $\varnothing$. It is natural to use 0 to denote the ordinal number determined by this well-ordered set. We refer to the ordinal numbers $0, 1, 2, \ldots, k, \ldots$ as the finite ordinals.

Let α and β be distinct ordinal numbers, and let X and Y be well-ordered sets of types α and β respectively. Then (since α and β are distinct) X is not similar to Y; and by 6.5(b), exactly one of these sets is similar to a section of the other. [Clearly: If X' and Y' are similar to X and Y respectively, then X' is similar to a section of Y' iff X is similar to a section in Y.]

Definition 6.6. Let α and β be ordinal numbers, and let X and Y be well-ordered sets of order types α and β respectively. Then α is *less than* β ($\alpha < \beta$) iff X is similar to a section in Y.

It is clear that the $<$ in 6.6 orders the finite ordinals just as the usual $<$ orders the non-negative integers. That is: If m and n are non-negative integers, then integer $m <$ integer n iff ordinal $m <$ ordinal n. Also, we see that the set $\{0, 1, 2, \ldots, n-1\}$ is well-ordered by $<$ and is of order type n. Thus, if n is a finite ordinal, then $\{x: \ x \text{ is an ordinal} < n\}$ has order type n. Our next theorem shows that this is true for any ordinal, finite or not.

Theorem 6.7. Let α be an ordinal number, and let $X = \{x: \ x \text{ is an ordinal} < \alpha\}$. Then X is well-ordered and has order type α.

Proof. Let Y be a well-ordered set of order type α. If $Y = \varnothing$, then $\alpha = 0$ and the conclusion is clear. Suppose then $Y \neq \varnothing$, and let $y \in Y$. The section $L(y)$ in Y is well-ordered and determines an ordinal number $f(y)$, which is clearly less than α. So $f(y) \in X$ for each y in Y, and we have a one-to-one map f of Y into X. To see that f is onto X, let $x \in X$. Then since $x < \alpha$, there is exactly one section $L(p)$ in Y which is of order type x. Then $f(p) = x$ and f is onto X. Clearly f preserves order, and X is similar to Y. Since Y is of order type α, so is X.

Theorem 6.8. Let X be a set of ordinal numbers. Then X is well-ordered.

Proof. Suppose $\varnothing \neq A \subset X$, and let $y \in A$. By 6.7, the set B of all ordinals $< y$ is well-ordered. If $A \cap B = \varnothing$, then y is the least element of A. But if $A \cap B \neq \varnothing$, then (as a subset of the well-ordered set B) $A \cap B$ must have a least element, which is clearly the least element of A. In either case, A has a least element, and X is well-ordered.

The set $\{0, 1, 2, \ldots\}$ of all finite ordinals is, by 6.8, well-ordered. The order type of this set is an ordinal number, which is usually denoted by ω. An ordinal α is called an *infinite* ordinal iff a well-ordered set of type α is an infinite set; α is *countable* iff a well-ordered set of type α is countable; α is *uncountable* is defined analogously.

It is easy to see that ω is the least (or first) infinite ordinal. [For suppose $\alpha < \omega$ and let Y be a well-ordered set of type α. Then Y is similar to a section in $\{0, 1, 2, 3, \ldots\}$, which is finite.]

Now $\{0, 1, 2, \ldots, \omega\}$ is well-ordered. If we use ω^+ to denote the order type of this set, then clearly $\omega < \omega^+$ and there is no ordinal between ω and ω^+. Similarly, if we use ω^{++} to denote the order type of $\{0, 1, 2, \ldots, \omega, \omega^+\}$, then ω^{++} is the "immediate successor" of ω^+, etc. Let α and β be ordinals. Then β is called the *immediate successor* of α iff (1) $\alpha < \beta$ and (2) there is no ordinal x such that $\alpha < x < \beta$. Also, α is called the *immediate predecessor* of β iff β is the immediate successor of α. Clearly: If α is an ordinal, then the order type of $\{x : x < \alpha \text{ or } x = \alpha\}$ is the immediate successor of α. So each ordinal has an immediate successor. [Name an ordinal which has no immediate predecessor.] (How about ω?)

Before describing other ordinals which do not have immediate predecessors, let us define addition of ordinal numbers. Let α and β be ordinals and let A and B be disjoint well-ordered sets of types α and β respectively. Let $C = A \cup B$ and order C as follows. For $x, y \in C$, $x < y$ iff (1) $x, y \in A$ and $x < y$ in A, (2) $x, y \in B$ and $x < y$ in B, or (3) $x \in A$ and $y \in B$. Clearly C is well-ordered. The order type of C is called the *sum* of α and β and is denoted by $\alpha + \beta$. The following remarks are easy to check.

Remark 6.9.

1. $1 + \omega = \omega$, but $\omega + 1 \neq \omega$.

2. If α is an ordinal, then $\alpha + 1$ is the immediate successor of α.

3. If α and β are ordinals, then $\alpha + \beta > \alpha$ when $\beta > 0$, and $\alpha + \beta > \beta$ or $\alpha + \beta = \beta$.

Suppose for each a in a well-ordered set A, x_a is an ordinal and X_a is a well-ordered set of order type x_a such that $X_b \cap X_c = \varnothing$ for each b, c in A with $b \neq c$. Let $X = \bigcup \{X_a : a \in A\}$, and order X such that $x < y$ iff (1) $x \in X_b$ and $y \in X_c$ with $b < c$ in A or (2) $x, y \in X_b$ for some b in A and $x < y$ in X_b. This well-orders X, and the order type of X is called the *sum* of the indexed collection $\{x_a: \quad a \in A\}$. In case A is N or N_k, we denote this sum by

$$x_1 + x_2 + x_3 + \ldots \quad \text{or by} \quad x_1 + x_2 + \ldots + x_k$$

respectively.

Remark 6.10.   Suppose for each i in N, x_i is an ordinal number. Then for each i in N,

$$x_i \leq x_1 + x_2 + x_3 + \ldots,$$

where $\leq$ means $<$ or $=$.

(Remark 6.10 follows from the fact that the well-ordered set $X = X_1 \cup X_2 \cup \ldots$ used to define $x_1 + x_2 + \ldots$ cannot be similar to a section in X_i. For an isomorphism of X onto a section in X_i would map some element of X_i onto a smaller element of X_i, leading to a contradiction of 6.2.)

The set

$$\{0, 1, 2, \ldots, \omega, \omega + 1, \omega + 2, \ldots, \omega + \omega, \omega + \omega + 1, \omega + \omega + 2, \ldots\}$$

has order type $\omega + \omega + \omega$ (if the dots are interpreted properly). Let $\alpha = \omega + \omega + \omega + \ldots$ (i.e., for each i in N, $x_i = \omega$). Then α is a countable ordinal. For this same α, $\alpha + \alpha + \alpha + \ldots$ (countably infinitely many terms) is still a countable ordinal.

Let X be the set of all countable ordinal numbers. By 6.8, X is well-ordered. The order type of X is denoted by Ω. If $\beta \in X$, then $\beta < \Omega$. [For $\{x: \quad x < \beta\}$ is a section in X of order type β. So $\beta < \Omega$ by 6.6.] So $\Omega \notin X$ (since Ω is not less than Ω). This means that Ω is not a countable ordinal (and hence X is not a countable set). But Ω is the first uncountable ordinal. For let $Y = \{y: \quad y < \Omega \quad \text{or} \quad y = \Omega\}$. Let α be the first uncountable ordinal in Y. (How do we know α exists?) Then $\{y: \quad y < \alpha\}$ is precisely the set of all countable ordinals. Hence α is Ω.

Theorem 6.11.   Let $X = \{x: \quad x \leq \Omega\}$, where $x \leq y$ means $x < y$ or $x = y$.

(a) If $A \subset X$, then there is a z in X such that $z = \sup A$ [i.e., (1) if $a \in A$, then $a \leq z$ and (2) if $y \in X$ such that $a \leq y$ for each a in A, then $z \leq y$].

(b) If A is a countable subset of X and $\Omega \notin A$, then $\sup A < \Omega$. If $A = \varnothing$, what is $\sup A$?

Proof of (b). Let $A = \{x_1, x_2, x_3, \ldots\}$ (if $A \neq \varnothing$), where the x_i's need not be distinct if A is finite. Since $\Omega \notin A$, each x_i is countable. So $x_1 + x_2 + x_3 + \ldots$ is countable. [Check the definition of such a sum.] By 6.10, this sum is an upper bound for A. Hence $\sup A$ (the least upper bound for A) is surely countable and so sup $A < \Omega$. (The proof of (a) is trivial.)

In 6.12, we summarize some of the important facts about ordinal numbers.

Theorem 6.12.   (a) ω is the first infinite ordinal, Ω is the first uncountable ordinal, and neither ω nor Ω has an immediate predecessor.

(b) The set of all countable ordinals is uncountable and has order type Ω.   (The set of all finite ordinals is infinite and has order type ω.)

(c) Each ordinal α has an immediate successor;   namely, $\alpha + 1$.

(d) If α is an ordinal, then $\{x:\ x < \alpha\}$ has order type α.

(e) None of the following ordinals has an immediate predecessor:

$$\omega,\ \omega + \omega,\ \omega + \omega + \omega + \omega,\ \omega + \omega + \omega + \ldots,$$
$$(\omega + \omega + \omega + \ldots) + \omega,\ (\omega + \omega + \omega + \ldots)$$
$$+ (\omega + \omega + \omega + \ldots) + (\omega + \omega + \omega + \ldots)$$
$$+ \ldots,\ldots,\ \Omega,\ \Omega + \omega,\ \Omega + \Omega.$$

Exercises 6.13

1. For each i in N, let x_i be an ordinal.   What is $x_1 + x_2 + x_3 + \ldots$ if for each i in N,

(a) $x_i = 1$?

(b) $x_i = 2$?

(c) $x_i = i$?

(d) x_i is a finite ordinal > 0?

2. What is

(a) $2 + \omega$?

(b) $2 + \Omega$?

(c) $\omega + \Omega$?

3. If α and β are ordinals, then $\alpha\beta$ (α times β) is defined by ordering $A \times B$ such that $(a, b) < (x, y)$ iff (1) $b < y$ or (2) $b = y$ and $a < x$, where A and B have order types α and β respectively. $\alpha\beta$ is defined to be the resulting order type of $A \times B$, which is clearly well-ordered.

(a) What is 2ω?   What is $\omega 2$?

(b) Show that if n is a finite ordinal > 0, then $n\omega = \omega$ while $\omega n = \omega + \omega + \omega + \ldots + \omega$ (n terms). [Indeed, the definition of $\alpha\beta$ was chosen so as to make $\alpha\beta$ equal to the result of "adding α to itself β times" (i.e., the sum of $\{x_a : a \in B\}$, where $x_a = \alpha$ for each a in a well-ordered set B of order type β).]

(c) For each i in N, let $x_i = \omega$. Prove:

$$x_1 + x_2 + x_3 + \ldots = \omega\omega.$$

7. Spaces Involving Ordinal Numbers

Throughout this section we let Y denote the set of all ordinal numbers less than Ω and we let $X = Y \cup \{\Omega\}$. In view of 6.8, both X and Y are simply ordered by the usual ordering in 6.6 of ordinal numbers.

If Z is a simply ordered set, the order topology for Z is the one with the open rays as a subbase. In this section we let X have the order topology and similarly for Y. [In general, if we speak of a space of ordinals, the order topology is understood.]

Exercises 7.1

1. Prove:

   (a) Y is first countable but not separable and hence not second countable.

   (b) X is not first countable.

2. Let $<$ be an anti-reflexive simple ordering in a set Z. (See 8 and 9 of 8.4 in Ch 2.) Let Z have the order topology.

   (a) Prove: Each closed subset of Z with both upper and lower bounds is compact iff Z is order complete. [To prove the if part, first use 1.8 to show that each "closed interval" $\{x : a \leq x \leq b\}$ is compact (under the hypothesis that Z is order complete).]

   (b) Prove: If Z is order complete, then each non-void subset of Z with a lower bound has a greatest lower bound (or infimum). [So the second half of 6.1 in Ch 2 actually follows from the first half.]

3. (a) Use 2 to show that X is compact.

   (b) Conclude: X is normal.

4. Prove:

   (a) Y is not compact.

   (b) Y is locally compact.

   (c) Y is countably compact.

It is interesting to note that 2(a) gives 4.1 in Ch 4 as a corollary, since R is order complete (by 6.1 in Ch 2). Compare this observation with the comment in 9(a) of 8.4 in Ch 2. These general exercises pinpoint the properties of R on which compactness and connectedness in R depend.

Proof of 4(c). Let A be an infinite subset of Y. Let B be a countable infinite subset of A. By 3, X is compact and hence countably compact. So B has a limit point p in X. By 6.11(b), $p < \Omega$. So p is a limit point of A in Y, and Y is countably compact.

Remark 7.2.   Let S and T be sequences in Y such that $S_i < T_i < S_{i+1}$ for each i in N. Then S and T converge to the same point in Y.

Proof. It is clear from 6.11(b) that $\Omega > \sup S[N] = \sup T[N]$. Clearly S and T converge to this point $\sup S[N]$.

Theorem 7.3.   The space Y is normal.

Proof. Let A and B be disjoint closed subsets of Y. Then (in X) $\Omega \notin A' \cap B'$. [For if $\Omega \in A' \cap B'$, then there are sequences S in A and T in B such that $S_i < T_i < S_{i+1}$. By 7.2, let $p \in Y$ such that S and T converge to p. Then $p \in A' \cap B'$; and since A and B are closed in Y, $p \in A \cap B$— a contradiction.] Suppose the labeling chosen so that $\Omega \notin B'$. Then B and $A \cup \{\Omega\}$ are disjoint closed subsets of X. By 3(b) in 7.1, let U and V be disjoint open subsets of X such that $A \cup \{\Omega\} \subset U$ and $B \subset V$. Then $U \cap Y$ and V are the desired disjoint open sets in Y.

We see from 7.1 and 7.3 that X is a compact normal T_2 space and Y is a locally compact normal T_2 space. It is interesting to note that, in spite of this, $X \times Y$ is not normal. For let $A = \{(x, x): x \in Y\}$ and let $B = \{(\Omega, x): x \in Y\}$. Suppose there were disjoint open sets U and V containing A and B respectively. To reach a contradiction, for each x in Y, let $f(x)$ be the least ordinal $> x$ such that $(f(x), x) \notin U$. Now $f(x) < \Omega$ because $(\Omega, x) \in B \subset V$ while $U \cap V = \emptyset$ and V is open. The following remark gives us the contradiction that some point (p, p) in the open set U is a limit point of $\{(f(x), x): x \in Y\}$, which is a subset of the complement of U.

Remark 7.4.   Let $f\colon Y \longrightarrow Y$ be a map such that $f(x) > x$. Then there is a point (p, p), with $p \in Y$, which is a limit point of $\{(f(x), x): x \in Y\}$.

Proof. Let S_1 be any point in Y. Inductively, let $T_i = f(S_i) > S_i$ and let $S_{i+1} = f(T_i) > T_i$. Let $p \in Y$ such that both sequences $S_1, S_2, S_3, \ldots$ and $T_1, T_2, T_3, \ldots$ converge to p. By 3.9 in Ch 5, the sequence (T_1, S_1), (T_2, S_2), $(T_3, S_3), \ldots$ converges to (p, p). Hence, by 3(a) in 2.3 of Ch 2, (p, p) is a limit point of $\{(f(x), x): x \in Y\}$.

It is fairly easy to see that X is completely normal. This implies that Y (and each subspace) is completely normal (and hence normal). So we also see that the product of two completely normal spaces need not be normal (and hence not completely normal).

We have already seen one normal space which is not completely normal. We would like to give another such space. (The earlier one is Q^Q.)

Let $Z = \{x: \ x \leq \omega\}$, where ω is the first infinite ordinal, and let Z have the order topology. Clearly Z is compact and T_2. So $X \times Z$ is compact and T_2 and hence is normal.

To see that $X \times Z$ is not completely normal, let $A = Y \times \{\omega\}$ and $B = \{\Omega\} \times [Z \sim \{\omega\}]$. Clearly A and B are separated. Suppose U and V are *any* open sets such that $A \subset U$ and $B \subset V$. For each x in $Z \sim \{\omega\}$, we have $(\Omega, x) \in B \subset V$. Since V is open, for each $x \neq \omega$ in Z, there is an element $f(x)$ in Y such that if $y > f(x)$ then $(y, x) \in V$. Since $\{f(x): x \in Z, x \neq \omega\}$ is countable, 6.11(b) gives us a point $p < \Omega$ such that

$$\{(y, x): \ x \in Z, x \neq \omega, y \in Y, y > p\} \subset V.$$

[Draw a figure.]

Now let $y_0 \in Y$ with $y_0 > p$. Since $(y_0, \omega) \in A \subset U$ and U is open, there is some $n < \omega$ such that

$$\{(y_0, z): \ n < z \leq \omega\} \subset U.$$

So $(y_0, z_0) \in U \cap V$ if $n < z_0 < \omega$. It follows that there are no disjoint open sets about A and B, and $X \times Z$ is not completely normal.

Here is another very instructive example:

Example 7.5. Let H be the "half-open" interval $[0, 1)$ in R, let $Z_0 = Y \times H$, and let Z_0 have the lexicographic (or dictionary) order [i.e., $(x, y) < (a, b)$ iff (1) $x < a$ or (2) $x = a$ and $y < b$]. Finally, let $Z = Z_0 \cup \{\Omega\}$, and let $\Omega > (x, y)$ for each (x, y) in Z_0. Let Z have the order topology.

It is easy to see that Z in 7.5 is simply ordered, is order complete, and has no gaps.

Remark 7.6. Let Z be the space in 7.5. Then:

(a) Z is connected [9(a) in 8.4 of Ch 2], compact [2(a) in 7.1], and T_2.

(b) Z is normal.

(c) $Z \sim \{p\}$ is connected iff $p = (0, 0)$ or $p = \Omega$.

(d) Z is not separable.

(e) Z is not metrizable.

Exercise 7.7

Let the unit square $Q \times Q$ have the lexicographic order and the resulting order topology. Compare this space with the one in 7.5. (Consider the properties listed in 7.6.)

8. Function Spaces

We considered earlier the product topology for the set Q^Q of all functions on Q to Q. It is quite common in analysis to be concerned with a set of functions and topological considerations in this set (such as the convergence of a sequence of these functions). This immediately suggests placing an appropriate topology on the set of functions as the underlying set. Then the machinery already developed for topological spaces will apply. Often there are two given spaces X and Y, and the set of functions under consideration is a subset F of the set Y^X of all maps of X into Y. One natural way to topologize F would be to treat F as a subspace of the product space Y^X. But the resulting topology is not the only useful topology for F.

We shall consider briefly an important special example of function spaces.

Remark 8.1.   Let (X, d_1) and (Y, d) be metric spaces, where d is a bounded metric for Y. Let F be the set of all maps of X into Y. For $f, g \in F$, let

$$e_1(f, g) = \sup \{d(f(x), g(x)): \quad x \in X\}.$$

Then e_1 is a metric for F.

The proof of 8.1 is trivial.

Theorem 8.2.   Let C be the set of all continuous members of the set F in 8.1 [where (X, d_1) and (Y, d) are the same as in 8.1]. Let (C, e) be the metric subspace of (F, e_1) [that is, for $f, g \in C \subset F$, $e(f, g) = e_1(f, g)$]. If Y is complete, then (C, e) is complete.

Proof. Let $f_1, f_2, f_3, \ldots$, be a Cauchy sequence in C. For a given x in X, the sequence $f_1(x), f_2(x), f_3(x), \ldots$ is a Cauchy sequence in Y [since $d(f_i(x), f_j(x)) \leq e(f_i, f_j)$]. Now Y is complete. So, for each x in X, let $f(x)$ be the unique point in the T_2 space Y to which $f_1(x), f_2(x), f_3(x), \ldots$, converges. Thus we have determined a map f of X into Y. So $f \in F$. [We shall show that $f \in C$. But first, we show that $f_1, f_2, f_3, \ldots$, converges to f in (F, e_1).]

Let $\epsilon > 0$. Since $f_1, f_2, \ldots$, is Cauchy, let $K \in N$ such that $e(f_i, f_j) < \epsilon/8$ for $i, j > K$. Suppose $x_0 \in X$. Since $f_1(x_0), f_2(x_0), \ldots$, converges to $f(x_0)$, let j be *some* particular integer $> K$ such that $d(f_j(x_0), f(x_0)) < \epsilon/8$. Let i be *any* integer $> K$. Then

$$d(f_i(x_0), f(x_0)) \leq d(f_i(x_0), f_j(x_0)) + d(f_j(x_0), f(x_0))$$

$$< e(f_i, f_j) + \frac{\epsilon}{8}$$

$$< \frac{\epsilon}{8} + \frac{\epsilon}{8} = \frac{\epsilon}{4}.$$

Since i was *any* integer $> K$ and K was chosen before x_0, it follows that: For *any* given $i > K$, $d(f_i(x), f(x)) < \epsilon/4$ for all x in X, and hence $e_1(f_i, f) \leq \epsilon/4 < \epsilon/3$ for all $i > K$. This means that $f_1, f_2, \ldots$ converges to f in (F, e_1).

Continuing with ϵ and K from above, to show $f \in C$, suppose $p \in X$. Let $i > K$. Since f_i is continuous at p, let $\delta > 0$ such that if $d_1(x, p) < \delta$ then $d(f_i(x), f_i(p)) < \epsilon/4$. Then if $d_1(x, p) < \delta$, we have

$$d(f(x), f(p)) \leq d(f(x), f_i(x)) + d(f_i(x), f_i(p)) + d(f_i(p), f(p))$$

$$< \frac{\epsilon}{4} + \frac{\epsilon}{4} + \frac{\epsilon}{4} < \epsilon.$$

Hence f is continuous at the arbitrary point p of X, and $f \in C$. So $f_1, f_2, f_3, \ldots$ converges to f in C, and 8.2 is proved.

We should note that the boundedness of Y in 8.1 and 8.2 was used only to conclude that sup $\{d(f(x), g(x)): \ x \in X\}$ exists in R. So if we replace the boundedness of Y by some other hypothesis which implies this supremum exists for all f, g in our set, then we still have the conclusions of 8.1 and 8.2. Thus we have the following corollary (since R is complete and Q is metric):

Corollary 8.3.   Let C be the set of all continuous maps of Q into R. For $f, g \in C$, let

$$d(f, g) = \sup \{|f(x) - g(x)|: \ x \in Q\}.$$

Then (C, d) is a complete metric space.

[We know that this supremum in 8.3 exists because $f - g$ is continuous on the compact set Q and hence is bounded.]

Next, we want to define the compact open topology for a set F of maps of a given space X into a given space Y. If $A \subset X$ and $U \subset Y$, let $K(A, U)$ denote $\{f: \ f \in F$ and $f[A] \subset U\}$.

Definition A.   Let F be a set of maps of a given topological space X into a given topological space Y. Let $\mathcal{S}$ be the family of all subsets of F of the form $K(A, U)$, where A is compact in X and U is open in Y. The topology for F which has $\mathcal{S}$ as a subbase is called the *compact open topology* for F.

Since each singleton set $\{p\}$ in X is compact, we have:

Remark B.   Let $\mathcal{T}$ be the product topology for the set Y^X of all maps of a space X into a space Y. Let $\mathcal{C}$ be the compact open topology for Y^X. Then $\mathcal{T} \subset \mathcal{C}$.

Corollary C.   Let $F \subset Y^X$ in Remark B. Let $\mathcal{F}$ be the relativization of $\mathcal{T}$ in Remark B to F. Then the compact open topology for F contains $\mathcal{F}$.

Proof. The compact open topology for F is the relativization of $\mathcal{C}$ in Remark B to F.

In connection with the compact open topology, it is usually a proper subfamily F of Y^X which is of interest, such as the family of all continuous maps of X into Y. Further results and references on the compact open topology may be found in Kelley's *General Topology* listed at the end of Ch 1.

Miscellaneous Exercises 8.4

1. Let e be the metric for Q^Q given in 8.1. Thus if $f, g \in Q^Q$, then
$$e(f, g) = \sup \{|f(x) - g(x)|: \quad x \in Q\}.$$
Let $\mathcal{F}$ be the e-metric topology for Q^Q, and let $\mathcal{T}$ be the product topology for Q^Q.

(a) Are these two topologies the same family? Is one of these a subfamily of (or smaller than) the other?

(b) For each n in N, let $f_n \in Q^Q$ such that $f_n(x) = 0$ if $x \neq 1/n$ while $f_n(1/n) = 1$. Let $f \in Q^Q$ such that $f(x) = 0$ for each x in Q. Does the sequence $f_1, f_2, \ldots$ $\mathcal{F}$-converge to f? Does this sequence $\mathcal{T}$-converge to f? Does this sequence $\mathcal{T}$- or $\mathcal{F}$-converge to some other point in Q^Q?

(c) Does one of these types of convergence imply the other?

(d) Is Q^Q $\mathcal{F}$-compact?

2. For each n in N, let $g_n \in Q^Q$ such that $g_n(x) = x^n$ for each x in Q. Let $g \in Q^Q$ such that $g(x) = 0$ if $x \in [0, 1)$ while $g(1) = 1$.

(a) Using the same notation as in 1, does the sequence $g_1, g_2, \ldots$ $\mathcal{T}$-converge to g? Does it $\mathcal{F}$-converge to g?

(b) Is $g_1, g_2, \ldots$ a Cauchy sequence in the space C of 8.3?

(c) Is the space C of 8.3 compact?

(d) Let $K = \{f: \; f \in Q^Q \text{ and } f \text{ is continuous}\}$. Is K an $\mathcal{F}$-compact subset of Q^Q? Is K a $\mathcal{T}$-compact subset of Q^Q? Is K a $\mathcal{C}$-compact space where $\mathcal{C}$ is the compact open topology for K?

(e) Is K a compact subset of the space C in 8.3?

3. Prove: The product space Q^Q is separable.

4. Let (X, d) be a metric space. Prove: If X is complete and totally bounded, then X is compact. [The converse has already been proved in separate parts.] [To prove X is countably compact (and hence compact), suppose A is an infinite subset of X. Since X is covered by a finite number of spheres with radius 1, we know that some such sphere, say S_1, contains infinitely many points of A. Let $p_1 \in S_1 \cap A$. Similarly there is a sphere S_2 of radius $\frac{1}{2}$ such that $S_2 \cap (S_1 \cap A)$ is infinite. Let $p_2 \in S_2 \cap S_1 \cap A$ such that $p_2 \neq p_1$. Continue inductively and obtain a Cauchy sequence of distinct points in A.]

Hint on 3. Let

$$\{[0, r_1), [r_1, r_2), [r_2, r_3), \ldots [r_{n-1}, r_n), [r_n, 1]\}$$

be a finite collection of intervals with rational end points. Let f be a map of Q into Q such that $f(x) = k_0$ for $x \in [0, r_1), f(x) = k_i$ for $x \in [r_i, r_{i+1})$ and $i = 1, 2, \ldots, n - 1$, and $f(x) = k_n$ for $x \in [r_n, 1]$, where each k_i is rational. (1) For the fixed collection of intervals, how many such functions are there? (2) How many such finite collections of intervals are there?

Let Y be the set of all functions obtained as above.

8

Nets and Convergence

We have spoken several times of the generalizing and abstracting process in mathematics. In this chapter we present a very simple example of this process and prove a few theorems concerning the resulting generalization. The main notion to be generalized here is that of convergence of a sequence to a point in a space. I have chosen this topic largely because of the importance of convergence in analysis and topology. (But I confess I was also tempted by its beauty and simplicity.) The work will be extremely easy for the now mature student (who has mastered much of the material in this book).

We recall that a sequence in a set X is a map of N into X. In our general theory of convergence, the generalization of a sequence in X—a "net in X"—will be a map of a "directed set A" into X, where "directed set A" is to be a generalization of N. To formulate a useful definition of "directed set" we must know which properties of N are essential to the convergence of a sequence. The convergence of a sequence S to a point is related to "the behavior of S_n as n becomes large" (as well as to the topology of the range space X). So the ordering in N is basic, and the question is: Which properties of the ordering are essential for a useful general theory of convergence?

1. Directed Sets and Nets

Definition 1.1.   Let A be a non-void set. A binary relation $\geq$ on A is said to *direct A* iff (a) $\geq$ is transitive and reflexive and (b) m, $n \in A$ implies there is a p in A such that $p \geq m$ and $p \geq n$.

Definition 1.2.   Let A be a non-void set and let $\geq$ direct A.   The pair $(A, \geq)$ is called a *directed set*.

Of course we often use the expression "the directed set A" to denote $(A, \geq)$.

Clearly N with its usual ordering is a special directed set.   Also the set of all subsets of a given set X is directed by $\subset$ ($B \geq C$ iff $B \subset C$).   Similarly $\supset$ directs the set of all subsets of X.   For another example, let $p \in X$, where X is a topological space.   Then $\subset$ directs the set of all neighborhoods of p.

Definition 1.3.   Let $(A, \geq)$ be a directed set and let f be a map of A into a set X.   Then f is called a *net in X* and is denoted by $(f, X, A, \geq)$.

So each sequence is a net but there are nets which are not sequences. We often denote $f(a)$ by f_a where $a \in A$.

Definition 1.4.   Let $(f, X, A, \geq)$ be a net, and let $Y \subset X$.

(a) f is *in Y* iff $f[A] \subset Y$.

(b) f is *eventually in Y* iff there is an m in A such that $f_n \in Y$ for each $n \geq m$ in A.

(c) f is *frequently in Y* iff for each m in A, there is a $p \geq m$ in A such that $f_p \in Y$.

2. Convergence of a Net in a Space

Definition 2.1.   Let $(f, X, A, \geq)$ be a net in X, where $(X, \mathscr{T})$ is a topological space.   Let $p \in X$.   Then f $\mathscr{T}$-*converges to p* iff f is eventually in each neighborhood of p.

We saw in 3 of 2.3 in Ch 2 that if there is a sequence in $A \sim \{p\}$ which converges to p, then $p \in A'$.   But the converse was not true in general, while the converse was true in first countable spaces.   The situation is different for nets.

Theorem 2.2.   Let $Y \subset X$ and $p \in X$, where X is a space. Then $p \in Y'$ iff there is a net in $Y \sim \{p\}$ which converges to p.

Proof. Suppose there is a net $(f, X, A, \geq)$ in $Y \sim \{p\}$ which converges to p. Let U be a neighborhood of p. Since f is eventually in U, there is an m in A such that $f_k \in U$ if $k \geq m$ in A, while $f_k \neq p$. Now $m \geq m$. So

$$f_m \in U \cap Y \sim \{p\} \quad \text{and} \quad p \in Y'.$$

Now suppose $p \in Y'$, and let A be the collection of all neighborhoods of p directed by $\subset$. For each U in A, let $f_U \in U \cap Y \sim \{p\}$—thus obtaining a net f in $Y \sim \{p\}$ which converges to p. [To see that f converges to p, let W be any neighborhood of p. Then for each V in A with $V \geq W$, $f_V \in V \subset W$. So f is eventually in W, an arbitrary neighborhood of p.]

Clearly $p \in Y^-$ iff there is a net in Y which converges to p.

Exercises 2.3

1. Let $(f, X, A, \geq)$ be a net, $p \in X$, and $\mathcal{S}$ a subbase for a topology for X. Prove: f converges to p iff f is eventually in each member of $\mathcal{S}$.

2. Let f be a net in a product space $\times \{X_a : a \in A\}$ and let x be a point in the product space. Prove: f converges to x iff $P_a \circ f$ converges to x_a for each a in A, where P_a denotes the ath projection map. [The directed set which is the domain of f may be denoted by $(B, \geq)$ since A denotes the index set.]

Definition 2.4.   Let f be a net in a space X and p a point in X. Then p is a *cluster point* of f iff f is frequently in each neighborhood of p.

We shall see that p may be a cluster point of a sequence S and yet there is no "subsequence of S" which converges to p.

Definition 2.5.   (a) Let S and T be sequences. T is a *subsequence of* S iff there is a sequence L in N such that (1) $T = S \circ L$ and (2) for each n in N, there is a k in N such that $L_i \geq n$ for $i \geq k$.

(b) Let $(f, X, A, \geq)$ and $(g, X, B, \geq')$ be nets. Then g is a *subnet of* f iff there is a map h of B into A such that (1) $g = f \circ h$ and (2) for each a in A, there is a k in B such that $h_b \geq a$ for $b \geq' k$.

Theorem 2.6.   Let $(f, X, A, \geq)$ be a net and x a point in a space X. Then x is a cluster point of f iff some subnet of f converges to x.

Proof. Because of (2) in (b) of 2.5, the if part is easy.

To prove the other half, suppose x is a cluster point of f. Let D be the family of all neighborhoods of x. Let

$$B = \{(a, U): \quad a \in A, \, U \in D, f_a \in U\}.$$

For $(a, U), (b, V) \in B$, let

$$(a, U) \geq' (b, V) \text{ iff } a \geq b \quad \text{and} \quad U \subset V.$$

(Show that $\geq'$ directs B.)   Let h be the map of B into A such that $h((a, U)) = a$.   Then $f \circ h$ is a subnet of f which converges to x.

Definition 2.7.   (a) Let $(A, \geq)$ be a directed set and let B be a subset of A.   Then B is a *cofinal* subset of A iff $a \in A$ implies there is some b in B such that $b \geq a$.

(b) Let h be a map of a directed set $(C, \geq')$ into a directed set $(A, \geq)$.   Then h is *isotone* iff $x \geq' y$ in C implies $h(x) \geq h(y)$.

Remark 2.8.   (a) Let h be an isotone map of a directed set B into a directed set A such that $h[B]$ is cofinal in A.   Let f be a net whose domain is A.   Then $f \circ h$ is a subnet of f.

(b) Let B be a cofinal subset of a directed set A (with the direction in A restricted to B) and let f be a net with domain A.   Then the restriction map of f to B is a subnet of f.

Part (b) is a corollary of (a) since: The identity map i [$i(x) = x$] of B into A is isotone; $i[B] = B$ is cofinal in A;   and $f \circ i$ is the restriction of f to B.   The type of subnet in (b) is called a *cofinal subnet*.   When trying to formulate a "good" definition of "subnet", it might at first seem natural to define a subnet as that which we have just called a cofinal subnet.   But if we do this, then 2.6 will not hold (see 2 and 3 in 2.9).

Exercises 2.9

1.   Let $X = \{x: \quad x \text{ is an ordinal} \leq \Omega\}$ with the order topology and let $Y = X \sim \{\Omega\}$.   Give an example of a net f in Y which converges to Ω.   Could f be a sequence?

2.   Let $X = [N \times (N \cup \{0\})] \cup \{(0, 0)\}$.   Let $\mathcal{T} = \{U: \quad U \subset X \text{ and}$ (1) $(0, 0) \in U$ implies U contains all but a finite number of the points $(n, 0)$ while (2) $(n_0, 0) \in U$ with $n_0 > 0$ implies U contains all but a finite number of the points $(n_0, m)\}$.   Then $\mathcal{T}$ is a topology for X.

Prove:

(a) There is a net in $N \times N$ which converges to $(0, 0)$.

(b) There is a sequence S in $N \times N$ which has $(0, 0)$ as a cluster point.

(c) There is a subnet of the sequence S in (b) which converges to $(0, 0)$.

(d) There is no sequence in $N \times N$ which converges to $(0, 0)$.

3. (a) Prove: Each subsequence of a sequence is a sequence.

(b) Observe that a subnet of a sequence may fail to be a sequence. See 2(c) and 2(d).

4.   Prove: If x is a cluster point of a net which is eventually in a closed set B, then $x \in B$.

From 2 and 3 in 2.9, we see that a sequence S may fail to have a subsequence which converges to a cluster point of S (although 2.6 implies there is a subnet of S which converges to this cluster point).   However, for first countable spaces, we have the companion theorem of 2.6 for sequences. Often the hypothesis of first countability allows us to replace "net" by "sequence" in a theorem.

Theorem 2.10.   Let x be a cluster point of a sequence S in a first countable space.   Then there is a subsequence of S which converges to x.

Proof.   Let $\{V_1, V_2, V_3, \ldots\}$ be a monotone decreasing countable local base at x.   For each i in N, let $k_i \in N$ such that $k_i > i$ and $S(k_i) \in V_i$.   Let $M = \{k_i : i \in N\}$.   Then M is cofinal in N, and the restriction of S to M is a subsequence of S which converges to x.

3.   Compactness in Terms of Nets

Lemma 3.1.   Let $(f, X, A, \geq)$ be a net in a space X.   For each a in A, let $Y_a = \{f(b) : b \geq a \text{ in } A\}$.   If $x \in \bigcap \{Y_a^- : a \in A\}$, then x is a cluster point of f.

Proof.   Suppose x is not a cluster point of f.   Hence there is some neighborhood U of x and some a in A such that $U \cap Y_a = \varnothing$.   So $x \notin Y_a^-$ for this a.   This proves the contrapositive of 3.1.

Theorem 3.2.   A space X is compact iff each net in X has a cluster point.

Proof. Suppose each net in X has a cluster point, and let $\mathcal{F}$ be a family of closed sets with FIP. Let $\mathcal{C} = \{B: \ B$ is the intersection of a finite subfamily of $\mathcal{F}\}$. Since the intersection of each two members of $\mathcal{C}$ is a member of $\mathcal{C}$, it follows that $\mathcal{C}$ is directed by $\subset$. For each C in $\mathcal{C}$, let $f(C) \in C$. By hypothesis, the net f thus obtained has a cluster point, say x. Let B be *any* member of $\mathcal{C}$. If $C \in \mathcal{C}$ with $C \subset B$ (i.e., $C \geq B$), then $f(C) \in C \subset B$. So f is eventually in the closed set B. By 4 in 2.9, $x \in B$. Since B is *any* member of $\mathcal{C}$, we have $x \in \bigcap \mathcal{C} \subset \bigcap \mathcal{F}$ since $\mathcal{F} \subset \mathcal{C}$. Hence $\bigcap \mathcal{F} \neq \varnothing$, and X is compact.

To prove the other half, suppose X is compact, and suppose $(f, X, A, \geq)$ is a net. For each a in A, let $Y_a = \{f_b: \ b \geq a$ in $A\}$. Then $\{Y_a: \ a \in A\}$ has the FIP. (Why?) So $\{Y_a^-: \ a \in A\}$ has the FIP. Since X is compact, there is some point y in $\bigcap \{Y_a^-: \ a \in A\}$. By 3.1, y is a cluster point of f and 3.2 is proved.

Corollary 3.3.   A space X is compact iff each net in X has a subnet which converges to some point in X.

Exercises 3.4

1. (a) Prove: If X is a countably compact T_1 space, then each sequence in X has a cluster point.

    (b) Give an example to show that T_1-ness in (a) cannot be dropped.

2. Give an example of a non-compact space X such that each sequence in X has a cluster point.

    [For 2, try a certain space of ordinal numbers.   The space in 4 of 4.9 in Ch 3 does the trick in 1(b).]

4.   Topologies Determined by Nets

In the preceding section we saw that compactness has a simple characterization in terms of nets. Indeed, for a fixed space $(X, \mathcal{T})$ one can completely determine the topology $\mathcal{T}$ if he knows which nets in X converge to which points. For (as observed just after 2.2) $p \in Y^-$ iff there is a net in Y which converges to p. From this, the closed sets and the open sets can be described as in the following exercises.

Exercises 4.1

1. Prove: A set Y in a space X is closed iff no net in Y converges to a point in $X \sim Y$.

2. Prove: A set U in a space X is open iff no net in $X \sim U$ converges to a point in U.

We saw in section 8 of Ch 2 that it is easy to give conditions which are such that a family C of subsets of a set X is the family of all closed sets relative to some topology for X iff C satisfies the given conditions.   We also found conditions which are necessary and sufficient for a "closure" function f to determine a topology for X such that $f(A)$ is the closure of A for each subset A of X.   There are notions other than openness, closedness and closure which may be used as the basic concept for a space.

The question arises: Is it possible to use convergence of nets as the basic notion?   That is, can we find an abstract rule of convergence which will determine a topology for a set X in such a way that a net f in X will topologically converge to a point p iff f converges to p according to the abstract rule of convergence?   The question is, what conditions must the rule of convergence satisfy?   These conditions are given in Kelley's *General Topology* and the desired results are proved there.

Miscellaneous Exercises 4.2

1. Let X be a set, and suppose some criterion is given which determines for each net f in X and each point p in X whether or not f "A-converges" to p (where "A-converges" is just a term used to mean f is paired with p).   What would be a natural way to specify the closed subsets of X in order to hope for a topology $\mathcal{T}$ for X such that $\mathcal{T}$-convergence coincides with A-convergence?   [Of course, the criterion for A-convergence must satisfy certain conditions in order that the proposed family of closed sets really determines a topology— not to mention the request that a net $\mathcal{T}$-converge to p iff it A-converges to p.   But we are not asking for these conditions on the criterion.   They are found in the above mentioned reference.]

2. (a) Give an example of a non-T_2 space X such that each sequence in X converges to at most one point in X.

    (b) Prove: A space X is T_2 iff each net in X converges to at most one point in X.

3. Let X be the space given in 2 of 2.9.   Let $f\colon N \times N \longrightarrow X$ be a map such that $f((m, n)) = (m, n)$.   For each m in N, let g_m or $\lim_n f(m, n)$ denote the unique point in X to which the sequence $f((m, 1)), f((m, 2)), \ldots$ converges.   Now let p or $\lim_m \lim_n f(m, n)$ denote the unique point in X to which the sequence $g_1, g_2, g_3, \ldots$ converges.

(a) What is the point p?

(b) Is there a map h of N into $N \times N$ such that $f \circ h$ converges to p?

Proof of the if part of 2(b). Suppose X is not T_2. There are distinct points p and q in X which do not have disjoint neighborhoods. Let $A = \{(U, V): U$ is a neighborhood of p and V is a neighborhood of $q\}$. Direct A by $\geq$, where $(U, V) \geq (W, Z)$ iff $U \subset W$ and $V \subset Z$. For each (U, V) in A, let $f_{(U,V)} \in U \cap V$—thus obtaining a net in X which converges to p and to q.

It should be stated that nets are often called *Moore-Smith sequences* or *generalized sequences.* The generalized convergence theory was initiated by E. H. Moore and H. L. Smith.

References: Moore-Smith Convergence

Chapter 2 of *General Topology* by J. L. Kelley (listed at the end of Ch 1 in this text).

J. L. Kelley, "Convergence in Topology," *Duke Math. J.* 17 (1950) 277–283.

E. J. McShane, "Partial Orderings and Moore-Smith Limits," *Amer. Math. Monthly* 59 (1952) 1–11.

E. H. Moore and H. L. Smith, "A General Theory of Limits," *Amer. J. Math.* 44 (1922) 102–121.

9

Peano Spaces

I. Continuous Curves

The notion of a continuous curve (Def 1.1) has been a fruitful one in set-theoretic topology. Most of us have heard the term "continuous curve" and we may have an intuitive idea about such curves in E_2 or E_3. What should be the formal definition?

For the case in E_2, C. Jordan gave a definition equivalent to the following: A subset A of E_2 is a continuous plane curve iff A is a continuous image of the closed unit interval. One might think that such a set A must have the intuitive property of "thinness" or "one dimensionality". But Peano shocked many of his colleagues in 1890 with a continuous map of the closed unit interval Q onto the closed unit square $Q \times Q$ in E_2. Indeed (as we shall see) $Q^n (= Q \times Q \times \ldots \times Q, n$ factors) is a continuous image of Q. A continuous map of Q onto Q^n is called a space-filling curve.

Definition I.I.   A topological space X is a *Peano space* (or *continuous curve*) iff X is T_2 and there is a continuous map of Q onto X.

156

An interesting problem is the topological characterization of Peano spaces, i.e., finding intrinsic topological properties of a T_2 space X which are equivalent to the existence of a continuous map of Q onto X. We now begin such a characterization, the end result being 6.1.

Definition I.2.   Let $C \subset A \subset X$, where X is a space. Then C is a *component of A* iff C is a maximal connected subset of A.

We use *lc* to mean "locally connected." In view of 1 and 2 in 5.8 of Ch 2, we have:

Remark I.3.   A space X is *lc* iff each component of each open subset of X is open.

Lemma I.4.   Let $f\colon X \longrightarrow Y$ be a continuous map. If C is a component of a subset U of $f[X]$, then $f^{-1}[C]$ is a union of components of $f^{-1}[U]$.

Proof. Let K be a component of $f^{-1}[U]$. Since $f[K]$ is connected, $C \cap f[K] = \varnothing$ or $f[K] \subset C$. Since each point of $f^{-1}[C]$ is in some component of $f^{-1}[U]$, 1.4 follows.

Lemma I.5.   If f is a continuous closed map of a *lc* space X onto a space Y, then Y is *lc*.

Proof. Let C be a component of an open set U in Y. Then $f^{-1}[C]$ is a union of some components of the open set $f^{-1}[U]$ (by 1.4). By 1.3, $f^{-1}[C]$ is open. So $X \sim f^{-1}[C]$ is closed. Since f is closed, $f[X \sim f^{-1}[C]] = Y \sim C$ is closed and C is open. By 1.3, Y is *lc*.

After proving 1.6, you may conclude 1.7 from 1.5 and 1.6.

Remark I.6.   Any continuous map of a compact space into a T_2 space is a closed map.

Theorem I.7.   The continuous image in a T_2 space of a compact *lc* space is a compact *lc* space.

Theorem I.8.   If f is a continuous map of a compact second countable space X onto a T_2 space Y, then Y is second countable (and compact and hence metrizable).

Proof. Let $\mathcal{B}$ be a countable base in X. Let $\mathcal{C} = \{U\colon U$ is the union of a finite subfamily of $\mathcal{B}\}$. By (β) near the end of section 3 in Ch 2, $\mathcal{C}$ is countable. By 1.6, $f[X \sim U]$ is closed for each U in $\mathcal{C}$. To see that the countable family
$$\{Y \sim f[X \sim U]\colon \quad U \in \mathcal{C}\}$$

is a base in Y, suppose $p \in V$, where V is open in Y.   Then

$$\text{the } closed \text{ set } f^{-1}[\{p\}] \subset \text{ the open set } f^{-1}[V].$$

Since $f^{-1}[\{p\}]$ is compact (?), it can be covered by a finite number of members of $\mathfrak{B}$ each of which is contained in $f^{-1}[V]$.   So there is a $U \in C$ such that

$$f^{-1}[\{p\}] \subset U \subset f^{-1}[V],$$

i.e.,
$$X \sim f^{-1}[\{p\}] \supset X \sim U \supset X \sim f^{-1}[V].$$

Hence
$$Y \sim \{p\} \supset f[X \sim U] \supset Y \sim V,$$

or
$$p \in Y \sim f[X \sim U] \subset V.$$

(That Y is metrizable follows from 4.7 in Ch 6.)

Since Q is compact, connected, lc and second countable, we combine 1.7 and 1.8 (and the invariance of connectedness under continuous maps) to obtain:

Theorem 1.9.   If X is a Peano space, then X is non-void, compact, connected, lc and metrizable.

The converse of 1.9 is also true.   So the conditions in the conclusion of 1.9 characterize Peano spaces.   The proof of the converse is in section 6, but sections 2 through 5 contain the preliminary details necessary for the solution of this problem.

2. Continua and Cut Points

Definition 2.1.   (a) Let X be a connected space.   A point p of X is a *cut point of X* iff $X \sim \{p\}$ is not connected; p is a *non-cut point of X* iff it is not a cut point of X.

(b) A space X is a *continuum* iff X is compact and connected and contains more than one point.

Theorem 2.2.   Let c be a cut point of a T_1 continuum X, and let $X \sim \{c\} = U \cup V$, where U and V are separated.   Then U contains a non-cut point of X, and so does V.

Proof.   Suppose the set of all non-cut points of X were contained in V. For each x in U, let $X \sim \{x\} = U_x \cup V_x$, where U_x and V_x are separated and $c \in V_x$.   By 3 in 5.8 of Ch 2, $U_x \cup \{x\}$ is connected.   Since $c \in V_x$,

$$U_x \cup \{x\} \subset U \cup V \quad \text{while} \quad x \in U.$$

So $U_x \cup \{x\} \subset U$ (by 2 in 5.4 of Ch 2). By HMP, let $\mathcal{C}$ be a maximal simply ordered subfamily of $\{U_x \cup \{x\}: \quad x \in U\}$ (ordered by set inclusion). We note that if $q \in U_x$ (where $x \in U$), then

(1) $\qquad\qquad U_q \cup \{q\} \subset U_x \quad \text{and} \quad x \notin U_q \cup \{q\}.$

[*Proof of* (1). One of the two connected sets $U_q \cup.\{q\}$ or $V_q \cup \{q\}$ does not contain x and hence must be contained in U_x or V_x. But $q \notin V_x$, so neither set is contained in V_x. Also $c \in V_q$ but $c \notin U_x$, so $V_q \cup \{q\} \not\subset U_x$. Thus (1) follows.]

In the T_1 space, $U_x \cup V_x$ is open. Since V_x is open in $U_x \cup V_x$, it follows that $\mathcal{C}$ is a collection of *closed* sets with the FIP. Since X is compact, let $p \in \bigcap \mathcal{C}$. Let $q \in U_p$. By (1), $U_q \cup \{q\}$ is a proper subset of each member of $\mathcal{C}$, and $\mathcal{C}$ is not maximal—a contradiction.

Corollary 2.3.   Each T_1 continuum contains at least two non-cut points.

Exercise

Prove: *Corollary 2.4.* If Y is the set of all non-cut points of a T_1 continuum X, there is no proper connected subset of X containing Y.

(*Proof.* Suppose $Y \subset Z \neq X$ and Z is connected. Let $c \in X \sim Z$. Then $X \sim \{c\} = U \cup V$, where U and V are separated. Since Z is connected, $Y \subset Z \subset U$ or $Y \subset Z \subset V$—contradicting 2.2.)

Definition 2.5.   Let p and q be distinct points of a connected space X.

(a) A point x *separates p and q in X* iff there are separated sets A and B such that $X \sim \{x\} = A \cup B$, $p \in A$ and $q \in B$.

(b) $S(p, q)$ denotes $\{x: \quad x = p, x = q, \text{ or } x \text{ separates } p \text{ and } q \text{ in } X\}$.

Remark 2.6.   Let $x, y \in S(p, q) \sim \{p, q\}$ in 2.5. Let $X \sim \{x\} = A_1 \cup B_1 = A_2 \cup B_2$, where A_i and B_i are separated, $p \in A_i$ and $q \in B_i$ for $i = 1, 2$. Let $X \sim \{y\} = C \cup D$, where C and D are separated, $p \in C$ and $q \in D$.

(a) If $y \in A_1$, then $C \cup \{y\} \subset A_2$. [Similarly if $y \in A_2$, then $y \in A_1$. Thus

$$A_1 \cap S(p, q) = A_2 \cap S(p, q).]$$

[Similarly $B_1 \cap S(p, q) = B_2 \cap S(p, q).$]

(b) If $y \in B_1$, then $A_1 \cup \{x\} \subset C$.

Proof.   (a) One of the connected sets $C \cup \{y\}$ or $D \cup \{y\}$ does not contain x and hence must be contained in A_1 or B_1.   Since $y \in A_1$, clearly $C \cup \{y\} \subset A_1$.   Thus $x \in D$.   Also $C \cup \{y\}$ or $D \cup \{y\}$ is contained in A_2 or B_2. Since $x \in D$, we must have $C \cup \{y\} \subset A_2$.

(b) Since $y \in B_1$, $B_1 \cup \{x\}$ can be contained in neither C nor D.   So $A_1 \cup \{x\} \subset C$.

Notation 2.7.   For each x in $S(p, q) \sim \{p, q\}$ of 2.6, let $P_x = A_1 \cap S(p, q)$ and let $F_x = B_1 \cap S(p, q)$, where A_1 and B_1 are as described in 2.6. [2.6(a) shows that P_x and F_x depend on x—not the particular A_1 and B_1.]

Definition 2.8.   The *separation* ordering for $S(p, q)$ in 2.5 is defined as follows:

(1) $p < z$ for each $z \neq p$ in $S(p, q)$.

(2) $z < q$ for each $z \neq q$ in $S(p, q)$.

(3) If $x, y \in S(p, q) \sim \{p, q\}$, then $y < x$ iff $y \in P_x$.

Clearly no element of $S(p, q)$ precedes itself.   Each pair of distinct points in $S(p, q)$ are comparable [2.6(b)].   Also $<$ is transitive [2.6(a)].   Thus:

Remark 2.9.   The separation ordering is an anti-reflexive simple ordering for $S(p, q)$ (by the definition given in 8 of 8.4 in Ch 2—which is consistent with 1.2 in Ch 7 when "simply ordered" is modified by the adjective "anti-reflexive").

See 9 in 8.4 of Ch 2 for the definition of order topology.

Theorem 2.10.   Let $(X, \mathcal{T})$ be a T_2 continuum with just two non-cut points p and q.   Then (a) $X = S(p, q)$, and (b) the separation order topology $\mathcal{F}$ is equal to $\mathcal{T}$.

Proof.   (a) Suppose $X \neq S(p, q)$.   Let $x \in X \sim S(p, q)$.   Since x is a cut point of X, let $X \sim \{x\} = U \cup V$, where U and V are separated.   Since $x \notin S(p, q)$, one of these separated sets, say U, contains $\{p, q\}$.   By 2.2, V contains a third non-cut point of X—a contradiction.   Thus $X = S(p, q)$.

(b) Let U be a left open ray in X (by the separation ordering).   By 2.8, $U = \varnothing$ $(= \{y: y < p\})$, $U = X \sim \{q\}$, or $U = P_x$, where $p < x < q$. Clearly $\varnothing$, $X \sim \{q\} \in \mathcal{T}$.   But P_x is the set A_1 in 2.6, and $A_1 \in \mathcal{T}$ (since A_1 is $\mathcal{T}$-open in the $\mathcal{T}$-open set $A_1 \cup B_1 = X \sim \{x\}$ in the T_1 space).   Similarly a right open ray is $\varnothing$, $X \sim \{p\}$, or F_x, each of which is $\mathcal{T}$-open.   Thus

(2) $\mathcal{F} \subset \mathcal{T}$

(since the open rays form a subbase for $\mathcal{F}$).

Suppose there is some $V \in \mathcal{T}$ but $V \notin \mathcal{F}$. Let $x \in V$ such that V contains no $\mathcal{F}$-neighborhood of x. Let $\mathcal{C}$ be the family of all "closed intervals" $[y, z]$ such that x belongs to the "open interval" (y, z) [unless (a) $x = p$, in which case $x \in [y, z)$ or (b) $x = q$, in which case $x \in (y, z]$]. Clearly

(3) $\bigcap \mathcal{C} = \{x\}$.

By (2), each member of $\mathcal{C}$ is $\mathcal{T}$-closed. So each member of

$$\mathcal{D} = \{[y, z] \cap (X \sim V): \quad [y, z] \in \mathcal{C}\}$$

is $\mathcal{T}$-closed. Also $\mathcal{D}$ has the FIP (since, for each $[y, z]$ in $\mathcal{C}$, $(y, z) \notin V$). Since X is compact, let

$$w \in \bigcap \mathcal{D} = \bigcap \{[y, z] \cap (X \sim V): \quad [y, z] \in \mathcal{C}\}.$$

Now $w \neq x$, since $x \in V$. This contradicts (3). Thus $\mathcal{T} \subset \mathcal{F}$. This with (2) implies $\mathcal{T} = \mathcal{F}$.

3. The Arc and the Simple Closed Curve

Before characterizing the Peano spaces, we solve a related problem—that of characterizing a homeomorph of Q. We then use this result to characterize a continuous image of Q in a T_2 space.

Definition 3.1.   (a) A space X is an *arc* iff X is homeomorphic to Q. The non-cut points of an arc are called the *end points*.

(b) A space X is a *simple closed curve* iff X is homeomorphic to the subspace

$$\{(x, y): \quad (x, y) \in E_2 \quad \text{and} \quad x^2 + y^2 = 1\} \quad \text{of } E_2.$$

Lemma 3.2.   Let A be a non-void, countable, anti-reflexive simply ordered set such that (a) A has no least element and no greatest element and (b) if $a, b \in A$ with $a < b$, there is some c in A such that $a < c < b$. Then A is order isomorphic to the set B of all rational numbers in the open interval $(0, 1)$ (ordered by the strict less than relation).

Proof. Let $K = \{k/2^n: \quad k, n \in N \text{ and } k < 2^n\}$, and let S be a one-to-one map of N onto A. Let $f(S_1) = \frac{1}{2}$. By (a), let n_1 and n_2 be the first integers such that

$$S_{n_1} < S_1 < S_{n_2}.$$

Let $f(S_{n_1}) = \frac{1}{4}$ and $f(S_{n_2}) = \frac{3}{4}$. By (a) and (b), let n_3, n_4, n_5 and n_6 be the first integers such that

$$S_{n_3} < S_{n_1} < S_{n_4} < S_1 < S_{n_5} < S_{n_2} < S_{n_6}.$$

Let $f(S_{n_3}) = \frac{1}{8}$, $f(S_{n_4}) = \frac{3}{8}$, $f(S_{n_5}) = \frac{5}{8}$ and $f(S_{n_6}) = \frac{7}{8}$.   Continuing, we obtain an order isomorphism of A onto K.

Since B satisfies the hypotheses on A, it follows that B is order isomorphic to K and hence to A.

Theorem 3.3.   A space X is an arc iff X is a metrizable continuum with just two non-cut points.

Proof.   The only if part is clear since Q is a metrizable continuum with just two non-cut points and these properties are topological invariants.

Suppose X is a metrizable continuum with just two non-cut points p and q.   Let A be a countable subset of $X \sim \{p, q\}$ such that $A^- = X$.   By 2.10, the space X is $S(p, q)$ with the separation order topology.   By 3.2, let f be an order isomorphism of A onto the set of all rationals in $(0, 1)$ [see 9(a) in 8.4 of Ch 2 and remember $A^- = X$].

Let $h(p) = 0$ and $h(q) = 1$.

Let $x \in X \sim \{p, q\}$.

Let

$$Y = \{y: \ y \in A \text{ and } y < x\}. \quad Y \neq \varnothing, \text{ so } f[Y] \neq \varnothing.$$

Let $h(x) = \sup f[Y]$.   Thus we obtain a one-to-one map h of X into Q which preserves order.

To see that h is onto Q, let $z \in (0, 1)$.   Let $W = \{w: \ w \text{ is rational and } 0 < w < z\}$.   Then $f^{-1}[W] \neq \varnothing$ and has an upper bound in X.   By 9(a) in 8.4 of Ch 2, let $s = \sup f^{-1}[W]$.   Then $h(s) = z$.   Hence h is an order isomorphism of X onto Q.   So h is a homeomorphism (since the topologies for X and Q are both the order topologies).

·Although our next theorem (like 2.4) is not part of our machinery for proving the main theorem of this chapter (the Hahn-Mazurkiewicz theorem), it is of interest and follows quickly from 3.3.

Theorem 3.4.   A space X is a simple closed curve iff X is a metrizable continuum such that, for each pair x, y of distinct points of X, $X \sim \{x, y\}$ is not connected.

Proof.   The only if part is clear.   Suppose then that X has the stated properties.   We note that:

(4)   If $x \in X$,   then $X \sim \{x\}$ is connected.

[*Proof.*   Suppose $X \sim \{x\} = U \cup V$, where U and V are separated.   In the T_1 space X, U and V are open.   So $U \cup \{x\}$ and $V \cup \{x\}$ are closed and hence are continua.   By 2.3, let $y \in U$ and $z \in V$ such that $U \cup \{x\} \sim \{y\}$ and $V \cup \{x\} \sim \{z\}$ are connected.   Then $X \sim \{y, z\}$ is connected, since it is the union of these two connected sets having x in common.   This is a contradiction.]

Now let $X \sim \{a\} \sim \{b\} = U \cup V$, where U and V are separated. By (4) and 3 in 5.8 of Ch 2, $U \cup \{b\}$ is connected. Similarly $U \cup \{a\}$ is connected. Hence $U \cup \{b\} \cup U \cup \{a\}$ is connected. Similarly $V \cup \{a, b\}$ is connected.

Suppose neither $U \cup \{a, b\}$ nor $V \cup \{a, b\}$ is an arc. Then by 3.3, there are points x in U and y in V such that x is a non-cut point of $U \cup \{a, b\}$ and y is a non-cut point of $V \cup \{a, b\}$. Then

$$X \sim \{x, y\} = (U \cup \{a, b\} \sim \{x\}) \cup (V \cup \{a, b\} \sim \{y\}),$$

which is connected (since it is the union of two connected sets having points in common). This contradicts a hypothesis.

Thus at least one of the sets $U \cup \{a, b\}$ or $V \cup \{a, b\}$ is an arc, say $U \cup \{a, b\}$. Suppose $V \cup \{a, b\}$ is not an arc, and again let $y \in V$ such that $V \cup \{a, b\} \sim \{y\}$ is connected. Let $z \in U$. Let $U \cup \{a, b\} \sim \{z\} = A \cup B$, where A and B are separated, $a \in A$ and $b \in B$. Then

$$X \sim \{y, z\} = A \cup B \cup (V \cup \{a, b\} \sim \{y\}),$$

which is connected, a contradiction.

Thus both $U \cup \{a, b\}$ and $V \cup \{a, b\}$ are arcs with end points a and b. Since X is the union of these two arcs (having only their end points in common), it follows that X is a simple closed curve.

4. Arcwise Connectivity

Definition 4.1.   (a) A finite family $\{L_1, L_2, \ldots, L_n\}$ of sets (called *links*) is a *simple chain from p to q* iff:

(1) $p \in L_i$ iff $i = 1$,

(2) $q \in L_i$ iff $i = n$,

(3) $L_i \cap L_j \neq \emptyset$ iff $|i - j| \leq 1$.

(b) Let $C = \{L_1, L_2, \ldots, L_n\}$ and $\mathcal{D} = \{M_1, M_2, \ldots, M_k\}$ be simple chains from p to q. $\mathcal{D}$ is a *simple refinement of* (or *simply refines*) C iff (1) each M_i is contained in some L_j and (2) if $M_s \subset L_j$ and $M_t \subset L_j$, then $M_i \subset L_j$ for each integer i between s and t.

(c) A space X is *arcwise connected* iff each pair of distinct points of X are the non-cut points of some arc contained in X.

Theorem 4.2.   Let (X, d) be a compact *lc* metric space. Let $\alpha > 0$. There is a $\delta > 0$ such that if $x, y \in X$ with $d(x, y) < \delta$, then $\{x, y\}$ is contained in a connected set of diameter less than α.

Proof. For each $p \in X$, let U_p be a connected neighborhood of p of diameter less than α (since X is *lc*). A Lebesgue number of the cover $\{U_p: \ p \in X\}$ is the desired positive number δ.

Lemma 4.3.   Let $\mathcal{C}$ be an open cover for a connected space X and let $p, q \in X$ with $p \neq q$. There is a simple chain of elements of $\mathcal{C}$ from p to q.

Proof. Let $Y = \{x: \ \text{there is a simple chain of elements of } \mathcal{C} \text{ from } p \text{ to } x\}$. $Y \neq \varnothing$ since $p \in Y$. It is an easy exercise to show that Y is open and Y is closed. Thus $Y = X$ and $q \in Y$.

Lemma 4.4.   Let $\mathcal{C} = \{U_1, U_2, \ldots, U_n\}$ be a simple chain of connected sets from p to q in a space. Let $\mathcal{A}$ be a family of open sets such that each U_i is a union of members of $\mathcal{A}$. Then there is a simple chain of members of $\mathcal{A}$ from p to q which simply refines $\mathcal{C}$.

Proof. Let $x_0 = p$ and $x_n = q$. For $i = 1, 2, \ldots, n - 1$, let $x_i \in U_i \cap U_{i+1}$. By 4.3 (applied to the subspace U_i), let $\mathcal{C}_i$ be a simple chain of elements of $\mathcal{A}$ from x_{i-1} to x_i, all links of $\mathcal{C}_i$ contained in U_i ($i = 1, 2, \ldots, n$). [The collection of all links of all the chains $\mathcal{C}_i$ may not form a simple chain from p to q, but it does contain such a chain.] In $\mathcal{C}_1$ there is a first link L which meets a link of $\mathcal{C}_2$, and there is a last link M in $\mathcal{C}_2$ which meets L. We omit the links of $\mathcal{C}_1$ after L and those of $\mathcal{C}_2$ preceding M. We thus obtain a simple chain $\mathcal{D}$ from x_0 to x_2. Now there is a first link G of $\mathcal{D}$ which meets a link of $\mathcal{C}_3$ and a last link H of $\mathcal{C}_3$ which meets G. We omit the links of $\mathcal{D}$ after G and those of $\mathcal{C}_3$ before H to obtain a simple chain from x_0 to x_3. It is now clear how we obtain the desired simple chain from p to q.

Remark 4.5.   Let X be a locally compact *lc* metric space. Let $r > 0$ and let $\mathcal{B} = \{U: \ U \text{ is open and connected while } U^- \text{ is compact and has diameter } < r\}$. Then $\mathcal{B}$ is a base for the metric topology for X.

Remark 4.6.   Let $\mathcal{C}$ be a non-void collection of closed connected subsets of a compact metric space X. If $\mathcal{C}$ is simply ordered by set inclusion, then $\bigcap \mathcal{C}$ is connected.

Proof. Suppose $\bigcap \mathcal{C} = A \cup B$, where A and B are separated. In the completely normal space X, let U and V be disjoint open sets such that $A \subset U$ and $B \subset V$.

Case I. Suppose for each C in $\mathcal{C}$, $C \cap (X \sim U \cup V) \neq \varnothing$. Then

$$\{(X \sim U \cup V) \cap C: \ C \in \mathcal{C}\}$$

is a family of closed sets with the FIP. Hence

$$\varnothing \neq \bigcap \{(X \sim U \cup V) \cap C: \quad C \in \mathcal{C}\} = (X \sim U \cup V) \cap (\bigcap \mathcal{C})$$
$$= (X \sim U \cup V) \cap (A \cup B)$$

—a contradiction.

Case II. Suppose $C_0 \cap (X \sim U \cup V) = \varnothing$ for some $C_0 \in \mathcal{C}$. Then

$$C_0 = (C_0 \cap U) \cup (C_0 \cap V)$$

while $C_0 \cap U$ and $C_0 \cap V$ are separated, contradicting the connectivity of C_0.

Theorem 4.7. Let X be a locally compact connected *lc* metric space. Then X is arcwise connected.

Proof. Suppose $p, q \in X$ and $p \neq q$. By 4.5 and 4.3, let $\mathcal{C}_1$ be a simple chain from p to q such that each link is open and connected and has compact closure of diameter < 1. By 4.4 and 4.5, let $\mathcal{C}_2$ be a simple chain from p to q which simply refines $\mathcal{C}_1$ and such that each link in $\mathcal{C}_2$ is open and connected and has compact closure of diameter $< \frac{1}{2}$. Inductively, for each i in N, let $\mathcal{C}_{i+1}$ be a simple chain from p to q which simply refines $\mathcal{C}_i$ and such that each link in $\mathcal{C}_{i+1}$ is open and connected and has compact closure of diameter $< 1/(i+1)$.

For each i in N, let $A_i = \{\bigcup L^-: \ L \in \mathcal{C}_i\}$. Clearly each A_i is compact and connected. Let $A = \bigcap \{A_i: \ i \in N\}$. Then A is a continuum containing p and q as non-cut points. [The connectivity of A follows from 4.6 (using the subspace A_1 as the compact space of 4.6).]

· Let $x \in A \sim \{p, q\}$. For each i in N, let $P_i = \bigcup \{L: \ L \in \mathcal{C}_i$ and L precedes the one or two links of $\mathcal{C}_i$ which contain $x\}$ and let $F_i = \{L : \bigcup L \in \mathcal{C}_i$ and L follows the one or two links which contain $x\}$. Let $P = \bigcup \{P_i: \ i \in N\}$ and $F = \bigcup \{F_i: \ i \in N\}$. Then $P \cap A$ and $F \cap A$ are non-void, disjoint and open in their union $A \sim \{x\}$. So x is a cut point of A. By 3.3, A is an arc from p to q.

Remark 4.8. An open subset of a compact T_2 space X is a locally compact subspace of X.

Corollary 4.9. A connected open subset of a compact *lc* metric space is arcwise connected.

Theorem 4.10. Let (X, d) be a *lc* metric continuum and let $\alpha > 0$. There is an $\epsilon > 0$ such that if $p, q \in X$ with $0 < d(p, q) < \epsilon$, then there is an arc from p to q of diameter $< \alpha$ (i.e., X is *uniformly locally arcwise connected*). ["From p to q" means p and q are the non-cut points.]

Proof. By 4.2, let $\epsilon > 0$ such that if $d(x, y) < \epsilon$, there is a connected set of diameter $< \alpha/2$ containing $\{x, y\}$. Let $p, q \in X$ with $0 < d(p, q) < \epsilon$. Let K be a connected set of diameter $< \alpha/2$ containing $\{p, q\}$. For each x in K, let G_x be a connected neighborhood of x of diameter $< \alpha/4$. Let $U = \bigcup \{G_x \colon x \in K\}$. Then U is a connected open set of diameter $< \alpha$, and $K \subset U$. By 4.9, there is an arc in U from p to q, and 4.10 is proved. [To see that U is connected, note that

$$U = \bigcup \{G_x \colon x \in K\} = \bigcup \{G_x \cup K \colon x \in K\},$$

and apply 1 in 5.8 of Ch 2.]

5. The Cantor Ternary Set

It is easily seen that for each x in Q, there is a sequence S in $\{0, 1, 2\}$ such that

$$x = \sum_{i=1}^{\infty} \frac{S_i}{3^i}.$$

It is convenient to use $:S_1S_2S_3 \ldots$ to denote the expression on the right and to call this a *triadic* or *ternary* expansion of x. Some numbers have two such expansions. $:2000\ldots$ and $:1222\ldots$ represent $\frac{2}{3}$. The only case in which a number has two triadic expansions is the one in which one expansion repeats zeros and the other expansion repeats twos from some place onward.

Definition 5.1.   The set $\{x \colon x \in Q$ and x has at least one ternary expansion in which the digit 1 does not occur$\}$ is called the *Cantor (ternary) set* [or the *Cantor discontinuum* or the *Cantor middle third set*] and is denoted here by T.

Remark 5.2. $T = \bigcap \{M_i \colon i \in N\}$, where $M_1 = Q \sim (\frac{1}{3}, \frac{2}{3})$, $M_2 = M_1 \sim [(\frac{1}{9}, \frac{2}{9}) \cup (\frac{7}{9}, \frac{8}{9})]$ and, for $i > 2$, M_i is obtained by deleting the middle third open intervals from the components of M_{i-1}.

[Remark 5.2 is clear because: The *open* middle third of Q is the set of *all* numbers in Q whose ternary expansions *must* have 1 in the "first digit" place.   The open middle thirds of $[0, \frac{1}{3}]$ and $[\frac{2}{3}, 1]$ consist of all numbers in Q whose triadic expansions must have 1 in the second place but not the first. Continuing, we see that T is obtained from Q by successive deletion of open middle third sets.]

Exercises 5.3

1. Prove: T is compact.   [Use 5.2]

2. A subset B of a space X is called a *retract of X* iff there is a continuous

map f: $X \longrightarrow B$ (called a *retraction*) such that $f(x) = x$ for each x in B. Prove: If A is a non-void closed subset of T, then A is a retract of T.

Proof of 2. For each p in T, there is a q in A such that $d(p, q) = d(A, p)$ [by 1(b) in 1.6 of Ch 6]. For each p in T where there are two such q's, let them be a_p and b_p with $a_p < p < b_p$. For each such p, let $y_p \in Q \sim T$ with $a_p < y_p < p$. For each x in $T \cap (y_p, b_p]$, let $f(x) = b_p$. Let $f(z) = a_p$ for each z in $T \cap [a_p, y_p)$.

For each t in T such that $f(t)$ is not determined by the preceding paragraph, there is just one q_t in A with $d(q_t, t) = d(A, t)$. Let $f(t) = q_t$ for each such t in T (if $f(t)$ was not determined above). The map f thus defined is the desired retraction.

Theorem 5.4. Each non-void compact metric space (X, d) is a continuous image of the Cantor set T. (Quite a theorem?)

Proof. Let $\mathcal{B} = \{U_1, U_2, U_3, \ldots\}$ be a countable base in X. For each n in N, let f_n be the map of $\{0, 2\}$ defined by $f_n(0) = U_n^-$ and $f_n(2) = X \sim U_n$.

For each x in T, let $:x_1 x_2 x_3 \ldots$ be the triadic expansion of x which has no 1 in it. For a fixed x,

$$\bigcap \{f_n(x_n): \quad n \in N\} = \varnothing$$

or is a singleton set $\{p_x\}$. [Prove this or see B at end of proof.] In the latter case, let $g(x) = p_x$; otherwise $g(x)$ is not defined. Let $A = \{x: g(x)$ is defined$\}$. Thus we have a map g: $A \longrightarrow X$. Clearly g is *onto* X [see C below]. Also [D below] g is continuous, and [E below] A is closed.

By 2 in 5.3, let h be a retraction of T onto A. Then $g \circ h$ is a continuous map of T onto X and 5.4 is proved (when the details are settled).

(B) Suppose $p, q \in X$ with $p \neq q$. Let $U_i \in \mathcal{B}$ such that $p \in U_i$ and $q \notin U_i^-$. Not both p and q belong to $f_i(x_i)$ since $f_i(x_i) = U_i^-$ or $X \sim U_i$.

(C) To see that g is onto X, let $p \in X$. Now $\bigcap \{U_i^-: \quad U_i \in \mathcal{B}$ and $p \in U_i\} = \{p\}$. Let $x = :x_1 x_2 x_3 \ldots$, where $x_i = 0$ if $p \in U_i$ while $x_i = 2$ if $p \notin U_i$. Then $g(x) = p$ and g is onto X.

(D) Let (without 1's) $:x_1 x_2 x_3 \ldots = x \in A$ and let $\epsilon > 0$. Let $U_k \in \mathcal{B}$ such that $g(x) \in U_k$ and U_k^- has diameter $< \epsilon$. Suppose (with no 1's) $:y_1 y_2 y_3 \ldots = y \in A$ with $|x - y| < 3^{-2k}$. Then

$$y_k = x_k \quad \text{and} \quad g(y) \in f_k(y_k) = f_k(x_k) = U_k^-.$$

So $d(g(y), g(x)) < \epsilon$. Thus g is continuous.

(E) Suppose $x \in T \sim A$. This means $\bigcap \{f_n(x_n): \quad n \in N\} = \varnothing$. Since each $f_n(x_n)$ is closed in the compact space X, we have (from 1.10 in Ch 4)

$\bigcap \{f_n(x_n): \ n \in N_m\} = \varnothing$ for some m in N. Let $y \in T$ such that $|x - y| <$
3^{-2m}. Then $y_n = x_n$ for $n \in N_m$. So

$$\bigcap \{f_n(y_n): \ n \in N_m\} = \varnothing \quad \text{and} \quad y \in T \sim A.$$

Hence $T \sim A$ is open in T, and A is closed.

6. The Hahn-Mazurkiewicz Theorem

Theorem 6.1.   A space X is a Peano space iff X is non-void, compact,
connected, lc and metrizable.

Proof.   Theorem 1.9 is the only if part.   Suppose then X has the properties listed.   Let d be a metric for X.   By 5.4, let f be a continuous map of
the Cantor set T onto X.   [We want to extend f to a continuous map g of
Q onto X.]   Let $g(x) = f(x)$ for each x in T.

Let $(a_1, b_1), (a_2, b_2), (a_3, b_3), \ldots$ be the (open interval) components of
$Q \sim T$.   If $f(a_n) = f(b_n)$, let $g(x) = f(a_n)$ for $x \in [a_n, b_n]$.

By 4.10, let $\epsilon_1 > 0$ such that if $0 < d(x, y) < \epsilon_1$, there is an arc from x
to y of diameter < 1.   Since f is uniformly continuous (on the compact set
T), there is a $\delta_1 > 0$ such that if $s, t \in T$ with $|s - t| < \delta_1$ then

$$d(f(s), f(t)) < \epsilon_1.$$

Thus there are at most a finite number of integers, say $n_1, n_2, \ldots, n_{k_1}$, such
that

$$d(f(a_{n_i}), f(b_{n_i})) \geq \epsilon_1.$$

By 4.7, let A_{n_i} be an arc in X from $f(a_{n_i})$ to $f(b_{n_i})$.   Now let g be extended
over each $[a_{n_i}, b_{n_i}]$ such that g (restricted to $[a_{n_i}, b_{n_i}]$) is a homeomorphism
onto A_{n_i}.

Again by 4.10, let $0 < \epsilon_2 < \epsilon_1$ such that if $0 < d(x, y) < \epsilon_2$, there is an
arc from x to y of diameter $< \frac{1}{2}$.   Again there is a $\delta_2 > 0$ such that if
$s, t \in T$ with $|s - t| < \delta_2$ then

$$d(f(s), f(t)) < \epsilon_2.$$

So there are at most a finite number of integers, say $m_1, m_2, \ldots, m_{k_2}$, such
that

$$\epsilon_2 \leq d(f(a_{m_i}), f(b_{m_i})) < \epsilon_1.$$

For each such m_i, let g be extended over $[a_{m_i}, b_{m_i}]$ to obtain a homeomorphism of $[a_{m_i}, b_{m_i}]$ onto an arc from $f(a_{m_i})$ to $f(b_{m_i})$ of diameter < 1.

By 4.10, let $0 < \epsilon_3 < \epsilon_2 < \epsilon_1$ such that if $0 < d(x, y) < \epsilon_3$, there is an
arc from x to y of diameter $< \frac{1}{3}$.   As before, there are at most a finite number
of our intervals $[a_j, b_j]$ for which

$$\epsilon_3 \leq d(f(a_j), f(b_j)) < \epsilon_2.$$

Let g be extended over these intervals to obtain a homeomorphism of each such $[a_j, b_j]$ onto an arc from $f(a_j)$ to $f(b_j)$ of diameter $< \frac{1}{2}$.

Then extend g over another finite number of intervals in $Q \sim T$ to obtain a homeomorphism of each onto an arc in X of diameter $< \frac{1}{3}$. Continuing in the above manner, we obtain a continuous map g of Q onto X. [Clearly $g[Q] = X$ since $f[T] = X$. Continuity of g follows since the diameters of the arcs used approach zero.]

Miscellaneous Exercises 6.2

1. Prove: Each Peano space is arcwise connected. [6.1 and 4.7].

2. (a) Give an example to show that arcwise connectivity is not a continuous invariant.

   (b) Let f be a continuous map of an arcwise connected space onto a T_2 space Y. Prove Y is arcwise connected. [For (b), use 1. For (a), give a trivial example in which the range space is indiscrete.]

3. Give an example of a T_2 continuum with just two non-cut points but which is not metrizable and hence not an arc. [Later, see 7.6 in Ch 7.]

4. Let $A = \{0, 2\}$ with the discrete topology. Let $Y = A^N$ with the product topology (where N is the set of all positive integers). Prove: The Cantor set T is homeomorphic to Y.

5. Give an example of a space X with a point p such that: (1) There is a neighborhood of p which contains no connected neighborhood of p. (2) Given any neighborhood U of p, there is a neighborhood V of p such that if $x \in V$, then $\{p, x\}$ is contained in a connected subset of U. [See the figure for such a subspace of E_2.]

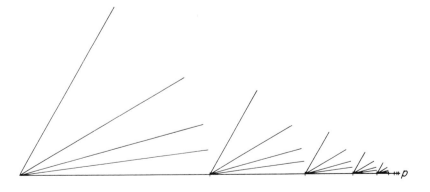

Index